11 Plus Verbal Ability Testbook

Author: Christine R. Draper

© P.R. and C.R. Draper 2016

This book was edited by Phillip Draper

All rights reserved. No part of this book may be reproduced or transmitted in any form or by any means without written permission of the author.

Published: achieve2day, Slough, 2016

ISBN: 978-1-909986-16-9

Verbal Ability - Test 1

Read the following excerpt from "The Secret Garden" by Frances Hodgson Burnett and answer the following questions.

1. At first each day which passed by for Mary Lennox was exactly like the others. Every morning
2. she awoke in her tapestried room and found Martha kneeling upon the hearth building her
3. fire; every morning she ate her breakfast in the nursery which had nothing amusing in it; and
4. after each breakfast she gazed out of the window across to the huge moor which seemed to
5. spread out on all sides and climb up to the sky, and after she had stared for a while she
6. realized that if she did not go out she would have to stay in and do nothing--and so she went
7. out. She did not know that this was the best thing she could have done, and she did not
8. know that, when she began to walk quickly or even run along the paths and down the
9. avenue, she was stirring her slow blood and making herself stronger by fighting with the
10. wind which swept down from the moor. She ran only to make herself warm, and she hated
11. the wind which rushed at her face and roared and held her back as if it were some giant she
12. could not see. But the big breaths of rough fresh air blown over the heather filled her lungs
13. with something which was good for her whole thin body and whipped some red colour into
14. her cheeks and brightened her dull eyes when she did not know anything about it.

15. But after a few days spent almost entirely out of doors she wakened one morning knowing
16. what it was to be hungry, and when she sat down to her breakfast she did not glance
17. disdainfully at her porridge and push it away, but took up her spoon and began to eat it and
18. went on eating it until her bowl was empty.

19. We have hundreds more books for your enjoyment. Read them all!

20. "Tha' got on well enough with that this mornin', didn't tha'?" said Martha.
21. "It tastes nice today," said Mary, feeling a little surprised herself.
22. "It's th' air of th' moor that's givin' thee stomach for tha' victuals," answered Martha. "It's
23. lucky for thee that tha's got victuals as well as appetite. There's been twelve in our cottage
24. as had th' stomach an' nothin' to put in it. You go on playin' you out o' doors every day an'
25. you'll get some flesh on your bones an' you won't be so yeller."
26. "I don't play," said Mary. "I have nothing to play with."

27. "Nothin' to play with!" exclaimed Martha. "Our children plays with sticks and stones. They
28. just runs about an' shouts an' looks at things." Mary did not shout, but she looked at things.
29. There was nothing else to do. She walked round and round the gardens and wandered about
30. the paths in the park. Sometimes she looked for Ben Weatherstaff, but though several times
31. she saw him at work he was too busy to look at her or was too surly. Once when she was

32. walking toward him he picked up his spade and turned away as if he did it on purpose.

33. One place she went to oftener than to any other. It was the long walk outside the gardens
34. with the walls round them. There were bare flower-beds on either side of it and against the
35. walls ivy grew thickly. There was one part of the wall where the creeping dark green leaves
36. were more bushy than elsewhere. It seemed as if for a long time that part had been
37. neglected. The rest of it had been clipped and made to look neat, but at this lower end of
38. the walk it had not been trimmed at all.

1. Who is Martha?
   a. Friend
   b. Housekeeper
   c. Sister
   d. Mother

2. Which of the following does Martha not spend her time doing?
   a. Playing with toys
   b. Reading books
   c. Running
   d. Looking at things

3. In line 33 it says "One place she went to oftener than to any other." Today, to be written correctly the word oftener would be replaced with:
   a. often
   b. more oftener
   c. often to
   d. more often

4. In line 22 the word "victuals" means
   a. intestines
   b. running
   c. food
   d. hunger

5. In line 32 the word spade is a
   a. verb
   b. noun
   c. adverb
   d. adjective

In the paragraph below choose the best word in each set of brackets, so that the paragraph makes sense.

While we are very [6](luck, grumpy, fortunate, well) in England, many people [7](through, throughout, over, at) the world live in [8](humble, dire, gross, viable) poverty. The lack of clean water is the cause of many [9](disease, illness, diseases, misery) which impair the ability of people to [10](improve, distress, enable, good) their situation. Another barrier to a better life is [11](there, their, they're, them) lack of access to a good education.

Underline the word on the right, goes with the words in both sets of brackets.

For example: (tree, branch) (glue, paste) stick, root, trunk, adhesive, flower
Answer: stick

12.   (sphere, round) (party, disco) moon, oval, ball, celebration, dance
13.   (water, dam) (fine, good) weir, well, great, happy, content
14.   (unfriendly, tease) (average, data) mode, mock, mean, nasty, dismal
15.   (clock, time) (look, view) minute, second, panorama, see, watch

Underline the word on the right which is closest in meaning to the word in bold on the left.

16.   **FASTEN**   server, secure, speedily, complete
17.   **PROUD**   humble, brash, arrogant, cheeky
18.   **ALTER**   publish, almost, temple, change
19.   **INCREASE**   gain, less, lessen, reduce
20.   **TRANSPARENT** see, open, opaque, clear

Dear Aunty Di,

I am writing to thank you for the lovely Christmas present. I have joined the school's chess club, so was anxious to play at home too.

   I really like the chess set though Dad was not so pleased last night when I beat him in a game. I think sitting by the warm fire while the rain beat on the window must have looked rather like a scene in a film.

   The only problem is that Alex is now crawling and Mum says that now he's mobile I need to be careful that he does not put any of the pieces in his mouth. However, Dad solved the problem by letting me put it on a shelf in his office, so it's nice and safe.

   I hope you are well. I have had a wonderful holiday but look forward to going back to school next week.

Love your niece,

Annabelle.

1. What was the weather like the night before she wrote the letter?
    a. Snowing.
    b. Raining.
    c. Fine.
    d. Warm and sunny.

2. What does Annabelle think of school?
    a. She likes it.
    b. She's indifferent.
    c. She doesn't like it.
    d. She only likes chess club.

3. Who is Alex?
    a. Her baby sister.
    b. Her baby brother.
    c. A pet.
    d. Her mum.

4. What does mobile mean in line 7?
    a. A toy placed above a baby's cot that turns in the air.
    b. A type of phone.
    c. Able to move around.
    d. A type of shop or library.

5. What word could be used to replace anxious in line 3?
    a. Nervous.
    b. Fearful.
    c. Keen.
    d. Eagerly.

6. What type of word is "the"?
    a. Noun.
    b. Pronoun.
    c. Definite article.
    d. Indefinite article.

Complete the passage below by filling in the missing letters.

Coffee is a brewed [7]be⬜⬜⬜age prepared from ground [8]b⬜⬜⬜s. It is [9]dr⬜⬜⬜ by many adults [10]ar⬜⬜⬜d the world. There is [11]ev⬜⬜⬜nce that people have been drinking coffee since the [12]fi⬜⬜⬜enth century if not before. Some people drink coffee so [13]reg⬜⬜⬜rly that when they don't they get a [14]head⬜⬜⬜e.

Antonyms

Choose the word which is most opposite to the word on the left.

15. **MEND**   fix, break, replace, hurt

16. **BALD**   ginger, hairy, fearful, shy

17. **ADORE**   hate, love, dare, before

18. **COMPULSORY**   frequent, option, optional, required

19. **CONCENTRATED** listen, dilute, silly, focus

20. **GENEROUS**   miser, median, ample, charitable

The Cookie Town Crumble

YOUR DAILY FAVOURITE NEWSPAPER

Winning Cake Crumbs

Sonya Gumbs

The winning cake before the thieves reduced it to crumbs.

Many were shocked and appalled today, at the Cookie Town's Community Hall. The prize winning cake, baked by Miss Budgerigar of Shakespeare Alley, was first noticed missing after the judging committee came back from lunch. The magnificent two foot round, brightly decorated cake was missing from its base. All the thieves left were a number of small crumbs.

"It was sabotage, pure and simple," sobbed Miss Budgerigar "I'm the best cake maker in the district, and they are all jealous of me." The police, who coincidentally and conveniently had a stall at the fair, started investigations.

"We have surveyed the scene and are making inquiries," said Sergeant Flour. "We will keep the public current with all developments".

The spirits of all were restored however by a wonderful afternoon tea, laid on by Lady Requisite of the Capital Tea house.

The photographic' competition was won this year by a Mister Daguerreotype, with a photograph of a French street scene with a person visible. "I had hoped that the reaction to this would not be negative", said Mr Daguerreotype.

The amateur art competition was won this year by Constable John, who painted a marvelous scene of the nearby Vales.

The raffle was won by Mrs Wager, who said she going to give the prize to her Aunty.

The day ended with the traditional display of Morris dancing, where handkerchiefs and bells were much in evidence.

1. What was happening today?
   a. The Cookie Town bake-off final.
   b. The Cookie Town Faire.
   c. The Police training programme.
   d. A photography workshop.

2. Who wrote the article
   a. Sonya Gumbs.
   b. Miss Budgerigar.
   c. Constable Flour.
   d. Constable John.
   e. The judges.

3. How long did the police take to get there, to investigate?
   a. A short time.
   b. They were already there.
   c. A couple of hours.
   d. The passage doesn't say.

4. What did the winning painting portray?
   a. A 2 foot round cake.
   b. A French street scene.
   c. A country fair.
   d. The local hills.
   e. Mr Daguerreotype.

5. When Sergeant Flour said ""We will keep the public current with all developments." What type of word is "keep"?
   a. Noun.
   b. Pronoun.
   c. Verb.
   d. Adjective.
   e. Article.

Complete the passage below by filling in the missing letters.

It was a ⁶gl⎕⎕⎕⎕⎕s Saturday afternoon and the sun was ⁷sh⎕⎕⎕⎕g in a ⁸cl⎕⎕⎕ blue sky. Brenda and a group of ⁹fr⎕⎕⎕ds went to the park to play basketball. ¹⁰Sud⎕⎕⎕ly the sky went dark and the sun had a bright ring around it. "Don't look said Saiwana, "It's a solar ¹¹e⎕⎕⎕⎕⎕e."

Jumbled Sentences

In the questions below, make a sentence using all the words apart from one. Underline the word which is not used.

12. he the same every caught the morning bus

13. had lead production he crew the the role theatre in

14. improve vocabulary to reading helps your learn

15. is up down ladder then it to than climb a climb easier

Complete the synonyms below.

16. **FLOWERED**   b l ⎕⎕⎕ o m e d

17. **MAKE**   c r ⎕⎕⎕ e

18. **CONFUSE**   b a ⎕⎕⎕ e

19. **FINE**   t ⎕⎕⎕

20. **BEFORE**   p r ⎕⎕⎕

Verbal Ability Test 4

Read the passage, and then answer the questions below:

Harvest Festival

Harvest festivals, when people give thanks for the harvest, are celebrated around the world. Many are religious festivals when people thank God for His provision and present the first fruits of the harvest.

In England, Harvest Festival is the Sunday closest to the Harvest moon which is referred to as Harvest Sunday. The harvest moon is the full Moon that occurs closest to the autumn equinox, occurring in September or the beginning of October.

Previously, Harvest festival was associated with the reapers accompanying a fully laden cart; a tradition of shouting "Hooky, hooky." Until the 20th century most farmers celebrated the end of the harvest with a big meal called the harvest supper, to which all who had helped in the harvest were invited. It was sometimes known as a "Mell-supper", after the last patch of corn or wheat standing in the fields which was known as the "Mell" or "Neck". Cutting it signified the end of the work of harvest and the beginning of the feast.

As British people have come to rely less heavily on home-grown produce, there has been a shift in emphasis in many Harvest Festival celebrations. Increasingly, churches have linked Harvest with an awareness of and concern for people in the developing world for whom growing crops of sufficient quality and quantity remains a struggle. Generally today, it is celebrated with hymns and people bringing in produce which is later distributed to local charities such as food banks, as well as collecting money for development aid agencies around the globe.

In the United States and Canada Harvest Festival has become a public holiday called "Thanksgiving." It is celebrated on the fourth Thursday of November in the United States and on the second Monday of October in Canada. Thanksgiving has many traditions in both countries, such as the eating of turkey. In Canada, Thanksgiving parades are common, the most well-known being the Kitchener-Waterloo Oktoberfest parade.

The origins of the Harvest Festival however are much older. The Jewish people have celebrated their Harvest Festival called the Sukkot, also called The Feast of the Tabernacles, for thousands of years.

In Roman times, the celebration of Cerelia, a harvest festival, was dedicated to the honour of Ceres. Ceres was their goddess of corn. It was also an autumnal festival held each year on October 4th. Offerings of the first fruits of the harvest and pigs were made to Ceres. The celebration included music, parades, games and sports and a thanksgiving feast.

Since the Mid-Autumn Festival coincides with the autumn harvest, the occasion is celebrated in Taiwan by making offerings to the Earth God Tu-ti Gong in hope that He will make the next year's harvest even more bountiful. Taiwanese harvest festival is called Tiong-cchiu Choeh, during this time people have picnics and climb mountains to have a better view of the moon. They eat moon cakes, as well as pomelos, or grapefruit. They pray to the moon god for protection, family unity, and good fortune.

The Homowo Festival, is a celebration of a traditional harvest festival from the Ga people of Ghana, West Africa, it is the largest cultural festival of its kind. For the Ga people, the word Homowo means "hooting at hunger." The origin of Homowo is tied to the origin of the Ga people and their migration to Ghana. The Ga travelled for many years before reaching the west coast of Africa where they now live. Along the way they experienced famine, but because they helped each other, they survived. Later when their harvests were bountiful, they held a feast at which they jeered at the hunger and hard times that had plagued them. This was the first Homowo.

So while there is a range of Harvest Festivals celebrated around the world. Perhaps the most popular with children is the mid-Autumn festival in Vietnam. In Vietnam, Têt-Trung-Thu or Trung Thu or the Mid-Autumn Festival is one of the most popular family holidays. It is held on the 15th day of the 8th lunar month. Vietnamese families plan their activities around their children on this special day. It is Vietnamese folklore that parents were working so hard to prepare for the harvest that they left the children playing by themselves. To make up for lost time, parents would use the Mid-Autumn festival as an opportunity to show their love and appreciation for their children. Appropriately, the Mid-Autumn Festival is also called the Children's Festival. Trung-Thu activities are often centred on children and education. Parents buy lanterns for their children so that they can participate in the lantern procession at dawn. Lanterns represent brightness while the procession symbolizes success in school. Vietnamese markets sell a variety of lanterns, but the most popular children's lantern is the star lantern. Other children's activities include arts and crafts in which children make face masks and lanterns. Children also perform traditional Vietnamese dances for adults and participate in contests for prizes and scholarships. Unicorn dancers are popular in Trung-Thu festivities, the dancers weave their way through the crowded streets to the accompaniment of drums and cymbals.

1. Choose the best sentence below based on the passage.
    a. All the traditions of Harvest Festival date back hundreds or even thousands of years.
    b. Harvest Festival celebrations have changed over the years.
    c. Harvest Festival is purely a religious festival.
    d. Harvest Festival is a day designed to raise money for charity.

2. When is Harvest Festival celebrated?
    a. On the Spring equinox.
    b. At the end of the harvest.
    c. October 4th.
    d. On a Thursday in November.

3. What could replace the word "reapers" in paragraph 3?
    a. Harvesters.
    b. Worshippers.
    c. Those celebrating.
    d. Recipients of the harvest.

4. Where is Harvest Festival also called the "Children's Festival"?
    a. Britain.
    b. Taiwan.
    c. Ghana.
    d. Vietnam.

5. Harvest Festival is a way of remembering history is some places. This is true in which of the following places?
    a. Britain.
    b. Taiwan.
    c. Ghana.
    d. Vietnam.

Complete the words in the passage below:

One evening as the sun was [6]s_ _ _ _ ng, the birds were [7]s_ _ _ _ ng and a

[8]p _ _ _   of moonlight covered the field, a little mouse peaked carefully out of her hole. Much

higher up on the [9]bo _ _ _   of a tree an owl was searching. Upon seeing the little mouse the owl

[10]sw _ _ _ ed down and clutched the mouse in her talons.

Compound words

Underline a word from each set of brackets to make a new, correctly spelled word.

11.	(sun, rain, sleet)	(beem, bow, fly)
12.	(time, run, go)	(send, cart, way)
13.	(fort, fore, for)	(tune, be, wart)
14.	(cat, cot, rat)	(his, her, ore)
15.	(cat, cot, sock)	(on, ton, tin)

Synonyms

Underline the synonym of the word on the left.

16.	**INHABIT**	house, find, holiday, occupy
17.	**IRATE**	angry, sad, ranking, ratio
18.	**DESTITUTE**	homeless, poor, fine, rich
19.	**SAVAGE**	domesticated, happy, wild, calm
20.	**SCENE**	saw, view, painting, play

Verbal Ability - Test 5

Read the following passage and answer the following questions.

1   In *"The Long Dark Tea-Time of the Soul,"* science-fiction author Douglas Adams shares the
2   opinion that "It can hardly be a coincidence that no language on earth has ever produced the
3   expression, 'As pretty as an airport'." Then again maybe being pretty is not what an airport is
4   about.
5
6   Let's take Heathrow for an example; in 2013 almost ten million people more than the whole
7   population of the United Kingdom departed or arrived through Heathrow airport. A whopping
8   72.3 million people were moved by Heathrow.
9
10 Heathrow, or as it was once called London Airport, has its origins back in the 1930's. It started
11 as a single grass runway, used for flight testing. Aircraft builder Richard Fairey paid the Vicar of
12 Harmondsworth £15,000 for part of the land, to build a private airport in which to assemble
13 and test aircraft.
14
15 During World War 2, a lot of the fighting was in the air, and an air base was built near the
16 ancient agricultural village of Heath Row; encompassing the private aerodrome of Richard
17 Fairey. Work did not start on RAF Heston until 1944, by which time another large base was
18 unneeded. So, in 1946 the site was handed over and London Airport was born.
19
20 The first flight that left from London Airport was bound for Buenos Aires, and by the end of the
21 year 63,000 people had flown into or out of London Airport.
22
23 From such humble beginnings we now have the wonder that is Heathrow today, over 70,000
24 people work at Heathrow, 4,500 of whom are employed directly by the British Aviation
25 Authority (B.A.A.). Travellers come from every corner of the globe into Heathrow coming from
26 180 destinations, from a total of 85 countries travelling on a staggering 82 different airlines.
27 The five most popular international destinations for passengers travelling from Heathrow are,
28 in order: New York, Dublin, Paris, Amsterdam and Frankfurt.
29
30 Together, Heathrow's two runways stretch for 4.7 miles, and they handle a total of almost 450
31 thousand flights a year. Heathrow never sleeps, even in the early morning, maintenance and
32 cleaning is carried out.
33
34 So even if Heathrow is not arguably pretty, one must say that it is pretty amazing.

1. London Airport is?
   a. The previous name for Heathrow Airport.
   b. An airport to the East of London.
   c. An air force base in Heston.
   d. The aerodrome built be Richard Fairley.

2. What was the population of the UK in 2013?
   a. 72.3 million.
   b. 64.1 million.
   c. 61.4 million.
   d. 81.4 million.

3. What does the author think of Heathrow?
   a. It is humble.
   b. They don't like it, as it isn't very pretty.
   c. It's grown too big.
   d. It's amazing.

4. Line 3 includes the saying "As pretty as an airport." The word pretty is a
   a. Noun.
   b. Verb.
   c. Adverb.
   d. Adjective.

5. In line 18 the word born is a
   a. Noun.
   b. Verb.
   c. Adverb.
   d. Adjective.

6. In line 16, another word for encompassing would be?
   a. Enclose.
   b. Including.
   c. Finding.
   d. Surrounding.

In the paragraph below underline the best word in each set of brackets, so that the paragraph makes sense.

While most people have a [7](natural, artificial, interesting, desire) ability to tell stories, few have the [8](pestilence, persistence, procrastinate, effort) and determination to become professional authors. Even fewer have the satisfaction of seeing their novels reach the top of the best-seller [9](row, column, lists, group). If you have the [10](want, desire, think, hopeful) to become the next J.K. Rowling, what should you do? The first thing [11](success, defer, desperate, successful) authors recommend is that you should read lots of books. Secondly, you should write [12](infrequently, often, hope, story).

Underline the word on the right, goes with the words in both sets of brackets.

For example: (tree, branch) (glue, paste)   stick, root, trunk, adhesive, flower
Answer: stick

13.   (alter, adapt) (money, coins)   edit, change, adjust, fee, cash

14.   (holiday, voyage) (stumble, fall)   cruise, outing, travel, lurch, trip

15.   (uninhabited, arid) (leave, abandon)   desert, populous, dessert, depart, vacate

Complete the antonyms below.

16. lead   f ☐☐☐ o w

17. deep   s h ☐☐☐ o w

18. appear   v ☐☐☐☐ h

19. artificial   n a ☐☐☐ a l

20. common   r ☐☐☐

Verbal Ability – Test 6

Read the first half of "The Golden Goose" and answer the following questions.

1   There was a man who had three sons, the youngest of whom was called Dummling, and was
2   despised, mocked, and sneered at on every occasion.

3

4   It happened that the eldest wanted to go into the forest to hew wood, and before he went his
5   mother gave him a beautiful sweet cake and a bottle of wine in order that he might not suffer from
6   hunger or thirst.

7

8   When he entered the forest he met a little grey-haired old man who bade him good day, and said:
9   'Do give me a piece of cake out of your pocket, and let me have a draught of your wine; I am so
10 hungry and thirsty.' But the clever son answered: 'If I give you my cake and wine, I shall have none
11 for myself; be off with you,' and he left the little man standing and went on.

12

13 But when he began to hew down a tree, it was not long before he made a false stroke, and the axe
14 cut him in the arm, so that he had to go home and have it bound up. And this was the little grey
15 man's doing.

16 After this the second son went into the forest, and his mother gave him, like the eldest, a cake and a
17 bottle of wine. The little old grey man met him likewise, and asked him for a piece of cake and a
18 drink of wine. But the second son, too, said sensibly enough: 'What I give you will be taken away
19 from myself; be off!' and he left the little man standing and went on. His punishment, however, was
20 not delayed; when he had made a few blows at the tree he struck himself in the leg, so that he had
21 to be carried home.

22

23 Then Dummling said: 'Father, do let me go and
24 cut wood.' The father answered: 'Your brothers
25 have hurt themselves with it, leave it alone, you
26 do not understand anything about it.' But
27 Dummling begged so long that at last he said:
28 'Just go then, you will get wiser by hurting
29 yourself.' His mother gave him a cake made with
30 water and baked in the cinders, and with it a
31 bottle of sour beer.

32

33 When he came to the forest the little old grey man met him likewise, and greeting him, said: 'Give
34 me a piece of your cake and a drink out of your bottle; I am so hungry and thirsty.' Dummling
35 answered: 'I have only cinder-cake and sour beer; if that pleases you, we will sit down and eat.' So
36 they sat down, and when Dummling pulled out his cinder-cake, it was a fine sweet cake, and the
37 sour beer had become good wine. So they ate and drank, and after that the little man said: 'Since
38 you have a good heart, and are willing to divide what you have, I will give you good luck. There
39 stands an old tree, cut it down, and you will find something at the roots.' Then the little man took
40 leave of him.

41

42 Dummling went and cut down the tree, and when it fell there was a goose sitting in the roots with
43 feathers of pure gold. He lifted her up, and taking her with him, went to an inn where he thought he
44 would stay the night.

1. What sort of story is "The Golden Goose?"
   a. A fairy tale
   b. Drama
   c. Adventure story
   d. Historical fiction

2. Why did Dummling get the cake made with water and sour beer, while his brothers got nicer food and drink?
   a. Dummling had a sensitive stomach
   b. Dummling may have been allergic to the other cake
   c. Dummling wasn't worth the extra expense
   d. His brothers were their parents favourite sons

3. What does "cinders," in line 35 mean?
   a. A character from a children's story
   b. The ash at the bottom of a fireplace
   c. Small bits of grass and leaves to start a fire
   d. Something that is of poor quality and often mocked

4. The author thought the older two sons' response to the little grey man was:
   a. Greedy
   b. Selfish
   c. Reasonable
   d. Guarded

5. What adjective could be used to describe the little grey man?
   a. Old
   b. Sly
   c. Aggressive
   d. Magic

Underline the correct word in each set of brackets, in the passage below.

Our Sun is a star. A star is a big ball of gas. It is in the middle of our [6](Solar, Solus, Stellar) System. Earth is the third [7](satellite, planet, asteroid) from the Sun.

The Sun is a long distance away from Earth. Light takes eight and a half minutes to travel from the Sun to Earth. It is this light [8](energy, power, force) that supports nearly all life on Earth.

The Sun is very large. Its diameter is nearly 110 times larger than Earth's diameter. However, it is [9](smaller, larger, biggest) than most stars. It is almost perfectly [10](circular, spherical, cuboid).

Choose the word that goes with both sets of brackets.

11. (horizontal, level) (house, apartment) plane, plain, home, mansion, flat

12. (type, breed) (caring, thoughtful) idea, species, variety, nice, kind

13. (piano, clarinet) (tissue, lung) organ, flute, trumpet, voice, heart

14. (dirty, stained) (sand, compost) grime, filth, ground, soil, humus

15. (bright, globe) (mass, delicate) illuminate, light, ignite, short, feint

Complete the word on the left, so that it means the opposite or nearly the opposite of the word on the right.

16. **SEPARATE**   m _ _ _ e

17. **WEALTH**   p _ _ _ r t y

18. **SCATTER**   g a _ _ _ r

19. **SUNSET**   s u n _ _ _ _

20. **CHILDISH**   m a _ _ _ _

Verbal Ability Test 7

Read the passage below, and then answer the questions that follow.

How an Orchestra Works

The orchestra is a musical ensemble that plays together to create beautiful music. There are four major instrument families that make up an orchestra: strings, woodwinds, brass, and percussion. A conductor leads the group from a podium in front of the ensemble.

Within the string family there are four instruments, listed in order from highest voice to lowest: violins, violas, cellos, and basses. These instruments are all played by moving a bow across the strings. These instruments typically sit in an arc in the front of the ensemble, closest to the audience, with first violins on stage left and second violins on stage right. In the orchestra, the concert master is second in command to the conductor and leads the majority of phrases and musical expression throughout the string section. The concert master is the first violinist and typically shakes the conductor's hand before the concert begins.

The woodwind family is the same as would be found in a wind band with the exception of saxophones, which are not included in orchestral instrumentation. There are two main types of woodwind instruments: flutes and reed instruments. They all make sound by air passing through a thin cylinder of wood, metal or plastic. The woodwind family members are: piccolo, flute, oboe, clarinet, English horn, and bassoon. The oboe gives the tuning note from which the ensemble tunes their instruments and checks intonation. The oboist is alerted to give the tuning note when the concert master stands.

Behind the woodwinds sit the brass: trumpet, French horn, trombone, and tuba. These instruments are placed at the back of the ensemble to help blend a more balanced sound as they contribute large volumes of sound. Brass instruments are all made of brass and consist of long pipes that widen at the end. They do not have a reed but are played by the musician vibrating their lips against a mouthpiece.

Finally, the percussion family is the largest in terms of instruments, but not in members. Some common percussion instruments are the timpani, bass drum, snare drum, marimba, xylophone, cymbals, tambourine, chimes and triangle. Percussion instruments include any instrument that makes a sound when it is hit, shaken, or scraped. There are two main types of percussion instruments: tuned and untuned. Percussion is most commonly set up either on the side of the ensemble or behind the brass.

Every member of the ensemble is important and must play their music accurately and expressively, under the conductor's direction, to create a beautiful sound and to perform the music well.

1. Which family contains the largest number of different instruments?
    a. The oboes.
    b. The strings.
    c. The percussion.
    d. The woodwind.

2. How are the different families of instruments classified?
    a. By how heavy the instruments are.
    b. By how each of the instruments look.
    c. By what material the instruments are made from.
    d.   By how each instrument produces sound.

3. Who leads the tuning of the ensemble?
    a. The saxophone.
    b. The flute.
    c. The piccolo.
    d. The oboe.

4. How is the orchestra organised?
    a. People read music and just play.
    b. The players follow the conductor's lead.
    c. They play how they feel the music should sound.
    d. Everybody follows the person on their left.

5. The brass sit behind the woodwind ...
    a. so that the sounds will blend, leading to a balanced result.
    b. so that they can be heard, seeing as they play so quietly.
    c. because that is where the instruments fit.
    d. because they have been naughty.

Complete the words in the passage below:

In England, the school year starts in [6]Sep _ _ _ _ _ r. It is [7]d _ _ _ _ _ d into three terms, each with a [8]h _ _ _ term break. The first term, also called the [9]A _ _ _ _ _ term, ends with the [10]Ch _ _ _ _ _ as holidays. The holidays at the end of the second term [11]us _ _ _ _ y include Easter. The final term ends with the long Summer holidays.

Compound words

Underline one word from each set of brackets, to make a new correctly spelled word.

12.   (fast, for, fear)   (ten, red, go)

13.   (pack, mist, miss)   (run, take, age)

14.   (car, trunk, tram)   (country, nation, tune)

15.   (so, she, me)   (in, an, it)

Synonyms

Complete the words on the right to form a word that means the same or nearly the same as the word on the left.

16.   **RIGID**   s _ _ _ f

17.   **BALANCE**   s t _ _ _ _

18.   **MISERY**   d _ _ _ a i r

19.   **INSIDE**   i n t _ _ _ _ r

20.   **HIDE**   c o n _ _ _ _

Verbal Ability Test 8

Below is the beginning of the poem, In Memoriam A.H.H., which was written by Lord Alfred Tennyson and published in 1850. It was written as a tribute to a close friend, who died as a young adult.

In Memoriam A.H.H.

1   Ring out, wild bells, to the wild sky,
2   The flying cloud, the frosty light:
3   The year is dying in the night;
4   Ring out, wild bells, and let him die.
5
6   Ring out the old, ring in the new,
7   Ring, happy bells, across the snow:
8   The year is going, let him go;
9   Ring out the false, ring in the true.
10
11   Ring out the grief that saps the mind,
12   For those that here we see no more;
13   Ring out the feud of rich and poor,
14   Ring in redress to all mankind.
15
16   Ring out a slowly dying cause,
17   And ancient forms of party strife;
18   Ring in the nobler modes of life,
19   With sweeter manners, purer laws.

1. What holiday would you associate with this poem?
   a. New Year
   b. Easter
   c. Remembrance Day
   d. Christmas

2. What does "feud" mean in line 13?
   a. An ongoing quarrel with bad feelings on each side
   b. A man-made waterway
   c. A home that has separate areas for servants
   d. The home of the Lord of the Manor

3. What does the word "redress" mean in line 14?
   a. To change clothes
   b. Correcting a wrong or injustice
   c. Playing holiday music
   d. Repeating what has been done before

4. What is the main theme of the poem?
   a. Sadness
   b. Renewal
   c. The ringing of bells
   d. Sadness and loss

5. Tennyson keeps repeating the words "ring out" at the beginning of each stanza. The word ring is:
   a. Noun
   b. Adjective
   c. Assonance
   d. Onomatopoeic

Underline the correct words in the passage below:

None of the [6](customers, inhabitants, adolescent) of the neighbourhood go past the old [7](derelict, deceived, horizon) house as it is said to be haunted. As the windows are broken and the walls are [8](shaking, sparkling, crumbling), it is also considered to be [9](danger, threatening, hazardous) to anyone brave enough to enter. The owners have let it fall into disrepair as they live abroad and only visit England to see an [10](aunt, uncle, relative) as he is their only family here.

Rearrange the word in bold to make a sentence which makes sense.

11. **LOSE**   There was a hole in the _____ of his shoe.

12. **LAMP**   He enjoyed relaxing under the _____ trees.

13. **NEAR**   He finally has a job and will _____ some money.

14. **STOP**   He couldn't wait for his birthday card to arrive in the _____.

15. **WHAT**   Make sure you _____ out the sausages well before cooking them.

Choose the word on the right which is most opposite to the word on the left.

16. **IMPORTANT**   worthy, necessary, small, insignificant

17. **SERIOUS**   trivial, fun, thoughtful, happy

18. **LAUGH**   chuckle, weep, shout, sing

19. **MODERN**   current, deter, ancient, passive

20. **ORDINARY**   astute, peculiar, plain, dinghy

Read the passage below about the Egyptian Hieroglyphic writing and answer the following questions.

The Egyptian hieroglyphic writing is among the oldest writing systems of the world. It was developed around the same time as the Sumerian cuneiform in Mesopotamia around 3200 B.C.. Egyptian hieroglyphs consisted of over 700 pictures, called hieroglyphs, which were used to represent objects, actions, sounds and ideas.

Hieroglyphs were written on lots of different surfaces, including: the walls of tombs and temples, monuments, pottery, wood and papyrus. Papyrus is the earliest paper, made from papyrus reeds: a water or marsh plant found by the banks of the river Nile. The hieroglyphs were written with a reed brush or pens and ink. The reed brushes were thin sharp reeds they would dip into the ink. The ink came from various coloured plants that they crushed and mixed with water.

For many years it was unknown how to read hieroglyphs. In 1799 the Rosetta Stone was found, in a small Egyptian village, called Rosetta. The Rosetta Stone is a stone that is written in three different scripts (two languages): hieroglyphics; demotic, the common script of Egypt and Greek. Scholars could use their knowledge of the demotic and Greek scripts to decode the hieroglyphics. However, it was 23 years before Jean-François Champollion deciphered the hieroglyphs after many years of studying the Rosetta Stone. The Rosetta Stone is thought to been carved in 196BC and was written by a group of Egyptian priests to honour the Egyptian pharaoh. It lists all of the things that the pharaoh had done that were good for the people of Egypt.

Reading hieroglyphics is not like reading English where the text is always written left to right. When reading hieroglyphics you need to look carefully at the direction the characters are facing. For example if an animal is facing to the right then the text should be read from right to left, but is the animal is pointing to the left then it should be read from left to right. Sometimes the hieroglyphics are written from top to bottom.

There are four different types of hieroglyphic signs. Word-signs represented objects. They were followed by an upward stroke. Alphabet-signs represented a single consonant sound. The hieroglyphic writing system was one without vowels so we do not know how many words sounded. Syllabic-signs represented two or three consonant sounds. There were also a number of determinatives which helped the reader interpret the writing. For example, if the word represented an abstract idea it was followed by a symbol depicting a roll of papyrus to show that the word could be expressed in writing but not pictorially. Some symbols could be used both as an alphabet-sign or a word-sign depending on the context and determinatives used. Hieroglyphs could also be combined to increase the meanings able to be portrayed.

So, hieroglyphics was an amazingly complex language, used by the Ancient Egyptians for over 3500 years. It had over 700 hieroglyphs that enabled one of the most powerful civilisations to develop.

1. About how long ago did the Egyptian hieroglyphics start?
   a. 3000 years ago.
   b. 4000 years ago.
   c. 5000 years ago.
   d. 6000 years ago.

2. Egyptian Hieroglyphs were:
   a. Pre-writing symbols used to depict objects and ideas.
   b. A written language.
   c. Decorations developed for the pyramids.
   d. Cave paintings.

3. Papyrus was made from:
   a. Paper.
   b. Reading.
   c. Reeds.
   d. A water plant that grew in aquariums.

4. The Rosetta stone enabled hieroglyphics to be deciphered because:
   a. Jean-François Champollion could speak ancient Egyptian.
   b. It contained new hieroglyphs that made sense of the ones already found.
   c. It was written about a pharaoh so its content was easy to understand from what we knew of Egyptian history.
   d. It contained two other scripts that could be compared to the hieroglyphs.

5. Each hieroglyph:
   a. Stood for an object or sound.
   b. Could have more than one interpretation.
   c. Was a part of the hieroglyphic alphabet.
   d. Was always written from top down.

Underline the correct word in each set of brackets, in the passage below.

In England children [6](must, advance, attend) nursery from three years of age. They are then [7](compulsory, required, additional) to remain in full-time education [8](until, since, after) they are 18. After sixteen they can go to school, college [9](and, or, but) participate in workplace learning schemes such as apprenticeships. Apprenticeships are a more [10](practical, practiced, practically) option for the less academically inclined.

Underline the two words which need to swap places in the sentence to make sense.

11. In Autumn trees leaves of many the fall.

12. Performance you maths improves your practicing.

13. It and cold is damp in Winter.

14. Leaves slowed the train track on the train down.

15. The Olympic young is the aspiration of many games athletes.

Synonyms

Underline the synonym of the word on the left.

16.	**SCAFFOLD**	building, ladder, framework, pipes
17.	**INTRICATE**	detailed, expensive, ostentatious, written
18.	**FOLIAGE**	lattice, leaves, station, follow
19.	**MOBILE**	toy, talk, move, communicate
20.	**ACQUIRE**	hoard, meet, dinner, purchase

Verbal Ability Test 10

Read the following excerpt from the Sherlock Holmes' story, "The Red-Headed League" by Sir Arthur Conan Doyle and answer the questions below.

The portly client puffed out his chest with an appearance of some little pride and pulled a dirty and wrinkled newspaper from the inside pocket of his greatcoat. As he glanced down the advertisement column, with his head thrust forward and the paper flattened out upon his knee, I took a good look at the man and endeavoured, after the fashion of my companion, to read the indications which might be presented by his dress or appearance.

I did not gain very much, however, by my inspection. Our visitor bore every mark of being an average commonplace British tradesman, obese, pompous, and slow. He wore rather baggy grey shepherd's check trousers, a not over-clean black frock-coat, unbuttoned in the front, and a drab waistcoat with a heavy brassy Albert chain, and a square pierced bit of metal dangling down as an ornament. A frayed top-hat and a faded brown overcoat with a wrinkled velvet collar lay upon a chair beside him. Altogether, look as I would, there was nothing remarkable about the man save his blazing red head, and the expression of extreme chagrin and discontent upon his features.

Sherlock Holmes' quick eye took in my occupation, and he shook his head with a smile as he noticed my questioning glances. "Beyond the obvious facts that he has at some time done manual labour, that he takes snuff, that he is a Freemason, that he has been in China, and that he has done a considerable amount of writing lately, I can deduce nothing else."

Mr. Jabez Wilson started up in his chair, with his forefinger upon the paper, but his eyes upon my companion.

"How, in the name of good-fortune, did you know all that, Mr. Holmes?" he asked. "How did you know, for example, that I did manual labour. It's as true as gospel, for I began as a ship's carpenter."

"Your hands, my dear sir. Your right hand is quite a size larger than your left. You have worked with it, and the muscles are more developed."

"Well, the snuff, then, and the Freemasonry?"

"I won't insult your intelligence by telling you how I read that, especially as, rather against the strict rules of your order, you use an arc-and-compass breastpin."

"Ah, of course, I forgot that. But the writing?"

"What else can be indicated by that right cuff so very shiny for five inches, and the left one with the smooth patch near the elbow where you rest it upon the desk?"

"Well, but China?"

"The fish that you have tattooed immediately above your right wrist could only have been done in China. I have made a small study of tattoo marks and have even contributed to the literature of the subject. That trick of staining the fishes' scales of a delicate pink is quite peculiar to China. When, in addition, I see a Chinese coin hanging from your watch-chain, the matter becomes even more simple."

Mr. Jabez Wilson laughed heavily. "Well, I never!" said he. "I thought at first that you had done something clever, but I see that there was nothing in it after all."

1. What is the name of the client?
    a. Mr Watson.
    b. Sherlock.
    c. Jabez.
    d. Name is not given in the text.

2. What is not true about the client?
    a. Chinese.
    b. Red hair.
    c. Overweight.
    d. Has worked as a ship's carpenter.

3. How does Sherlock Holmes come across in the passage?
    a. Questioning.
    b. Combative.
    c. Observant.
    d. Quick runner.

4. When was the story set?
    a. 12th Century.
    b. 19th Century.
    c. 21st Century.
    d. 25th Century.

5. What was the mood of Mr Wilson?
   a. Happy.
   b. Unhappy.
   c. Angry.
   d. Scared.

Complete the words in the passage below.

In England speeding is very common. A [6]q _ _ _ _ er of all deaths on our roads are

[7]c _ _ _ ed by speeding. 55% of drivers speed on the motorway, but the most [8]co _ _ _ _

place to speed is on our urban [9]st _ _ _ ts. While most accidents and injuries occur on urban

roads it is in [10]r _ _ _ l areas that there are the most fatalities.

Find a word that rhymes with the word on the left to complete the sentence.

11. **ROAR**   They had a lovely time by the sea _____.

12. **STOVE**   The flower was a lovely _____ colour.

13. **FLUSH**   I had to _____ because I was running late.

14. **FAST**   The _____ of actors were very talented.

15. **GUM**   It really hurt when I hit my _____ with the hammer.

Choose the word on the right which is most opposite to the word on the left.

16. **VAGUE**   precise, crisp, showy, unclear

17. **FLAT**   apartment, hilly, horizontal, plane

18. **READ**   learn, grow, write, draw

19. **EXPAND**   grow, elongate, sole, contract

20. **ENTER**   door, window, depart, delay

Verbal Ability Test 11

Below is an excerpt from the book "Little Women," by Louisa May Alcott. Little Women is a story about the four March sisters: Meg, Jo, Beth and Amy. This excerpt centres around Beth who is portrayed in the story as quiet and shy but kind and thoughtful and their wealthy next-door neighbour Mr James Lawrence.

1   But Beth, though yearning for the grand piano, could not pluck up courage to go to the 'Mansion of
2   Bliss', as Meg called it. She went once with Jo, but the old gentleman, not being aware of her
3   infirmity, stared at her so hard from under his heavy eyebrows, and said "Hey!" so loud, that he
4   frightened her so much her 'feet chattered on the floor', she never told her mother, and she ran
5   away, declaring she would never go there any more, not even for the dear piano. No persuasions or
6   enticements could overcome her fear, till, the fact coming to Mr. Laurence's ear in some mysterious
7   way, he set about mending matters. During one of the brief calls he made, he artfully led the
8   conversation to music, and talked away about great singers whom he had seen, fine organs he had
9   heard, and told such charming anecdotes that Beth found it impossible to stay in her distant corner,
10 but crept nearer and nearer, as if fascinated. At the back of his chair she stopped and stood
11 listening, with her great eyes wide open and her cheeks red with excitement of this unusual
12 performance. Taking no more notice of her than if she had been a fly, Mr. Laurence talked on about
13 Laurie's lessons and teachers. And presently, as if the idea had just occurred to him, he said to Mrs.
14 March...
15
16 "The boy neglects his music now, and I'm glad of it, for he was getting too fond of it. But the piano
17 suffers for want of use. Wouldn't some of your girls like to run over, and practice on it now and
18 then, just to keep it in tune, you know, ma'am?"
19
20 Beth took a step forward, and pressed her hands tightly together to keep from clapping them, for
21 this was an irresistible temptation, and the thought of practicing on that splendid instrument quite
22 took her breath away. Before Mrs. March could reply, Mr. Laurence went on with an odd little nod
23 and smile...
24
25 "They needn't see or speak to anyone, but run in at any time. For I'm shut up in my study at the
26 other end of the house, Laurie is out a great deal, and the servants are never near the drawing room
27 after nine o'clock."
28
29 Here he rose, as if going, and Beth made up her mind to speak, for that last arrangement left
30 nothing to be desired. "Please, tell the young ladies what I say, and if they don't care to come, why,
31 never mind." Here a little hand slipped into his, and Beth looked up at him with a face full of
32 gratitude, as she said, in her earnest yet timid way...
33

34   "Oh sir, they do care, very very much!"

35

36   "Are you the musical girl?" he asked, without any startling "Hey!" as he looked down at her very
37   kindly.

38

39   "I'm Beth. I love it dearly, and I'll come, if you are quite sure nobody will hear me, and be
40   disturbed," she added, fearing to be rude, and trembling at her own boldness as she spoke.

41

42   "Not a soul, my dear. The house is empty half the day, so come and drum away as much as you like,
43   and I shall be obliged to you."

44

45   "How kind you are, sir!"

46

47   Beth blushed like a rose under the friendly look he wore, but she was not frightened now, and gave
48   the hand a grateful squeeze because she had no words to thank him for the precious gift he had
49   given her. The old gentleman softly stroked the hair off her forehead, and, stooping down, he kissed
50   her, saying, in a tone few people ever heard...

51

52   "I had a little girl once, with eyes like these. God bless you, my dear! Good day, madam." And
53   away he went, in a great hurry.

1. What does the word "yearning" in line 1 mean?
   a. Reaching.
   b. Desiring.
   c. Fever.
   d. Concerning.

2. What does the sentence in lines 5-7; "No persuasions or enticements could overcome her fear, till, the fact coming to Mr. Laurence's ear in some mysterious way, he set about mending matters." convey to the reader?
   a. The reader believes that what is happening in the Laurence house is mysterious.
   b. The reader understands that Mr Laurence will not succeed in persuading or enticing.
   c. The reader understands that Mr Laurence has a problem with his ear which the doctors have been unable to diagnose.
   d. The reader understands Mr Laurence's intentions even though Beth does not.

3. What adjective could be used to describe the actions and words of Mr Laurence in lines 49-50? "The old gentleman softly stroked the hair off her forehead, and, stooping down, he kissed her, saying, in a tone few people ever heard..."
   a. Affectionate.
   b. Grumpy.
   c. Hurried.
   d. Respectful.

4. In lines 25 and 26 why does Mr Laurence say, "They needn't see or speak to anyone, but run in at any time. For I'm shut up in my study at the other end of the house?"
   a. He doesn't want to be disturbed.
   b. No one is around anyway.
   c. He is trying to create a situation in which Beth will be comfortable.
   d. He is informing Beth of the rules of the mansion, so she does not offend.

5. What is the central idea of the passage?
   a. Beth needs help to learn to play the piano.
   b. Mr Laurence wants to hear music in the house again and finds out Beth can play.
   c. Beth wants to play the piano in front of her neighbours.
   d. My Laurence enables Beth to overcome her fear and do something she loves.

Underline the correct words in the passage below:

When Diedre [6](sat, wrote, made) a test she did not do very well, as she had not [7](revise, revisited, revised). She was not pleased with her result and [8](either, neither, nor) was her teacher, who made her resit it. This [9](means, meant, mint) that she could not go to her [10](friend, friend's friends) party as her parents made her study instead.

Rearrange the words below so that all the words, except one, makes a sentence that makes sense. Underline the word that does not fit into the sentence.

11. stop arrived minutes the late bus ten

12. broke leg hospital needed he he his crutches so

13. he sat the a of to book shade sunny read his tree under

14. its rotates moon axis every day Earth on

15. hockey stick Tuesday played after every he school

Complete the antonym

16. **START**   c _ _ _ l u _ _

17. **ABOUT**   e _ _ _ t

18. **FIRST**   _ _ n a _

19. **QUESTION**   r _ p _ _

20. **SMALL**   _ _ s s i _ _

Verbal Ability – Test 12

Read the passage below about bacteria and answer the following questions.

1 Bacteria are the smallest type of organisms. An average bacterium is only about a thousandth of a
2 millimetre. This is too small to be seen with the naked eye. They consist of a single cell, which is
3 much smaller and simpler in structure than other cells such as animal cells.

4

5 Bacteria were first discovered by Antonie van Leeuwonhoek, who developed a more powerful
6 microscope. Using his hand-crafted microscopes he was the first to observe and describe single-
7 celled organisms, which he originally referred to as animalcules. He was also the first to record
8 microscopic observations of muscle fibres, bacteria, and blood flow in capillaries (small blood
9 vessels).

10

11 Bacteria are everywhere – in air, water, soil and other organisms. While they like warmth some can
12 survive in ice while others live in hot springs with temperatures over 80°C. Bacteria are so
13 numerous that there are more bacteria than all the other organisms put together. Further, the
14 mass of bacteria is greater than the mass of all the other organisms put together.

15

16 Some bacteria are helpful. Bacteria are used to make yoghurt and cheese. Many bacteria in our
17 intestines help to keep us healthy. Bacteria have even been used to clean up oil-spills. Humans
18 have in recent years modified bacteria to work for us. Perhaps, the most well-known example is the
19 use of bacteria to produce human insulin for use by diabetics. Unfortunately, not all bacteria are
20 healthy for us. Bacteria can emit toxins which can damage tissue and cause sickness. Some
21 diseases caused by bacteria include bacterial tonsillitis (sore throat), tuberculosis and cholera.

22

23 So while we might not often think about it, there is an invisible living world all around us.

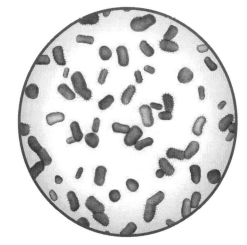

1. Which of the following is not true?
   a. They are too simple to modify.
   b. They are extremely small.
   c. They are single celled.
   d. They can be used to clean up oil spills.

2. That bacteria can live within other organisms:
   a. Is good, as it keeps our intestines healthy.
   b. Is bad because bacteria are germs and cause disease.
   c. Can be good or bad depending on the type of bacteria.
   d. The passage doesn't say.

3. The word helpful in line 16 could be replaced by:
   a. ubiquitous
   b. benevolent
   c. nice
   d. beneficial

4. The word emit in line 20 is a
   a. Noun
   b. Verb
   c. Adverb
   d. Adjective

5. What is the purpose of this passage
   a. To entertain
   b. To inform the reader about bacteria
   c. To persuade the reader that not all bacteria are bad
   d. To provide humour

Complete the words in the passage below.

On the fifth of [6]N _ _ _ _ _ er 1605, Guy Fawkes and his companions [7]l _ _ _ ed a cellar

[8]i _ _ _ _ i _ tely below the House of Lords. They filled the cellar with [9]ba _ _ _ _ s

of gunpowder, which were covered with wood and coals to increase the force of the

[10]ex _ _ _ _ _ on. We remember this act of treason as Guy Fawkes Day or Bonfire Night.

Underline the word that goes with both sets of brackets..

11. (sit, walk)   (holder, bracket)   stand, crouch, crawl, frame, file

12. (bed, couch)   (head, president)sofa, bench, chair, stool, convener

13. (file, entry)   (tape, album)   query, data, documentation, list, record

14. (branch, leaf)   (source, origin)   tree, root, bark, sap, start

15. (grade, mark)   (flat, horizontal)percent, merit, achieve, plane, level

Complete the synonym

16. **NECK**   t _ _ _ a t

17. **BREAK**   s m _ _ _

18. **STEM**   _ _ a l _

19. **GRIP**   _ _ u t _ h

20. **CHEER**   a p _ _ _ _ d

Verbal Ability – Test 13

The Monkey and the Dolphin: A tale attributed to Aesop.

A Sailor, bound on a long voyage, took with him a Monkey to amuse him while on shipboard. As he sailed off the coast of Greece, a violent tempest arose, in which the ship was wrecked, and he, his Monkey and all the crew were obliged to swim for their lives. A Dolphin saw the Monkey contending with the waves, and supposing him to be a man (whom he is always said to befriend), came and placed himself under him, to convey him on his back in safety to the shore. When the Dolphin arrived with his burden in sight of land not far from Athens, he demanded of the Monkey if he were an Athenian, who answered that he was, and that he was descended from one of the noblest families in that city.

The Dolphin then inquired if he knew the Piræus (the famous harbour of Athens). The Monkey, supposing that a man was meant, and being obliged to support his previous lie, answered that he knew him very well, and that he was an intimate friend, who would, no doubt, be very glad to see him. The Dolphin, indignant at these falsehoods, dipped the Monkey under the water, and drowned him.

1. A tempest is a:
   a. Sea monster.
   b. Ship's voyage.
   c. Storm.
   d. Large wave.

2. Why was the monkey the dolphin's burden?
   a. The dolphin was carrying the monkey.
   b. The monkey was not honest with the dolphin.
   c. It meant the dolphin had to swim towards Athens.
   d. The monkey was not human.

3. What is the Piræus?
   a. An ancestor of the monkey.
   b. A descendant of the monkey.
   c. A famous Athenian.
   d. A harbour.

4. What type of word is the word "intimate," in the second paragraph.
   a. Noun.
   b. Verb.
   c. Adjective.
   d. Adverb.

5. What is the moral of this story?
   a. Be nice to dolphins and they will be nice to you.
   b. If you start to tell lies, you will be obliged to tell more.
   c. A burden shared is a burden halved.
   d. If you do not know the answer, do not answer at all.

Underline the correct words in the passage below:

Jeremiah cycled [6](panic, frantically, frivolously, randomly) up the hill. He quickly looked behind him, but they were gaining distance and he could feel his speed [7](increasing, decreasing, quicken, lengthen). Sheer panic gripped him. He had to think of [8](someone, anymore, something, idea) quickly, or it would be [9](to, too, two, way) late. Just in time he [10](sees, senses, thinks, saw) a gate.

In the questions below, A, B and C are in alphabetical order. The word B is missing and a dictionary definition is given instead. Write word B in the space provided.

11. a. IDEALLY

    b. _ _ _ _ _ _ _ _ _   exactly the same.

    c. IDIOCY

12. a. EMAIL

    b. _ _ _ _ _ _ _ _ _   cause someone to feel awkward, self-conscious or ashamed.

    c. EMBED

13. a. NEURON

    b. _ _ _ _ _ _ _   impartial or unbiased.

    c. NEVER

14. a. DIFFICULT

    b. _ _ _ _ _ _   to break down food.

    c. DIGIT

15. a. LADDER

    b. _ _ _ _ _   an implement used for serving out soup

    c. LAGOON

Underline the word that is opposite to the word in bold.

16. **STUBBORN**   obstinate, mule, help, flexible

17. **PECULIAR**   odd, usual, often, hurried

18. **VULNERABLE**   robust, brittle, nimble, vigorous

19. **OBJECT**   thing, thought, agree, dinghy

20. **OUTSTANDING**   rich, mediocre, except, lowing

Verbal Ability – Test 14

Read the passage below and then answer the following questions.

1   Matthew looked up to the building and felt his stomach twist. It was his first day attending this
2   school, and everything was different from what he knew. The new school building was larger than
3   the one from his previous school, and the students and teachers were people he hadn't met before.

4   Standing outside the glass doors, held open by a woman who smiled as others passed her by, his
5   legs trembled. Matthew wanted to go back home, where things weren't so strange and new. He
6   took a step back.

7   "Ow!" another student said. Matthew turned to see that there was another boy there, someone
8   who looked about his age, and he had stepped on his foot. The boy pouted and ran through the
9   doors, into the building. Matthew wondered if he had made him mad....

10   It was then the lady at the door spoke. "It will be all right," she said, her voice gentle. "Now, hurry
11   inside."

12   He nodded his head and made his way inside, to the assembly hall. On the way there, the main
13   hallway was lined with the students, talking and laughing with one another before classes began.
14   Matthew remembered how he had done the same with his friends, before they all had to go to
15   different schools. Now he was alone. After assembly he walked to class.

16   "Hey!" someone said ahead of him. It was the boy from before, standing in an open doorway to a
17   class. The class he was supposed to go to.

18   He couldn't run away, so he apologised again and hoped the boy would forgive him. "I'm really
19   sorry about stepping on your foot."

20   "It doesn't hurt anymore." The boy rubbed the back of his head. "I was nervous too, so I wasn't
21   looking where I was going. So, I'm sorry too."

22   Matthew felt a little better and introduced himself. "I'm Matthew."

23   "I'm Ken," the boy said back.

24   The lady from before came from inside the class. She was his new teacher. With a smile, she told
25   him, "I told you it would be all right. Now, come and join your class."

26   Matthew smiled, and the churning in his stomach finally stopped. He stepped into his new
27   classroom to start the first day of many in the school.

1. In the first line, what does it mean by Matthew's stomach twisted?
   a. He felt unwell.
   b. He felt nauseous.
   c. He was nervous.
   d. He was excited.

2. In lines 11 to 14, how does Matthew feel?
   a. Scared.
   b. Excited.
   c. Cheerful.
   d. Lonely.

3. Stepping on the boy's foot in line 8, was going to:
   a. Make settling in very difficult.
   b. Mean others won't talk to him.
   c. Get him into trouble.
   d. Have no lasting consequence.

4. The word introduced in line 21 is a
   a. Noun.
   b. Verb.
   c. Adverb.
   d. Adjective.

5. What is the purpose of this passage
   a. To entertain.
   b. To inform.
   c. To persuade.
   d. To record events.

Complete the words in the passage below.

During and after the First World War there were terrible food

[6]s h _ _ _ _ _ e s. These meant that many people became

[7]m a _ _ _ _ _ i s h e d. Also, to buy any food, meant

standing in a very long [8]q _ _ _ _. It was only in 1918 that

food [9]r a _ _ _ _ i n g was introduced, to try and

[10]im _ _ _ _ e the situation.

Food
1 = buy it with thought
2 = cook it with care
3 = serve just enough
4 = save what will keep
5 = eat what would spoil
6 = home-grown is best
don't waste it

Find a letter that ends the first word and starts the second word. Must be the **same** letter in each set of brackets.

11. f a s (   ) r a m   r a (   ) u g

12. f o r (   ) o r e   c a l (   ) a d e

13. w o o (   ) a m e   b a l (   ) a m b

14. s t e (   ) a s t   f l i (   ) o o r

15. s t o n (   ) v e r y   h o l (   ) y e

Synonyms

Underline the word that is most like the word in bold.

16. **HOLE**   pit, pith, all, dig

17. **APPARENT**   possible, might, seeming, tricky

18. **VAGUE**   uneven, certain, conceal, unclear

19. **PERMIT**   fine, consent, consist, prohibit

20. **CRAFTY**   art, drawing, cunning, meek

Verbal Activity Test 15

Read the passage below about the history of the Paralympics then answer the questions.

 The word Paralympic comes from the Greek work para, meaning beside and Olympic. This illustrates how the Paralympics and the Olympics exist side by side. Today the Paralympic Games is the biggest sports' event for disabled athletes in the world. In London, at the 2012 Games, 4302 athletes from 164 countries competed in 20 sports which were televised around the world.

However, the origins of the Paralympics are far humbler. There were athletes with disabilities in the Olympic Games, such as German American gymnast George Eyser in 1904, who had an artificial leg; Hungarian Karoly Takacs, a right-arm amputee who competed in shooting events in both the 1948 and 1952 Olympics and Lis Hartel, a Danish equestrian athlete who had contracted polio in 1943 and won a silver medal in the dressage event. However, their numbers were extremely small.

It was not until after World War Two that sports for disabled people became more common and started to be more widely acknowledged. In 1944, Dr. Ludwig Guttmann opened a spinal injuries centre at the Stoke Mandeville Hospital, UK. Dr Guttmann was very concerned about how to overcome the commonly held view that once paralysed a person held a pointless future and strove to restore hope and self-worth in his patients. One way he did this was through the medium of sport. On the 29th of July 1948, the day of the Opening Ceremony of the London 1948 Olympic Games, Dr. Guttmann organised the first competition for wheelchair athletes, to compete in archery, which he called the Stoke Mandeville Games. 16 people competed, a cup was presented and the first official competition for disabled athletes had occurred.

The Stoke Mandeville Games took place yearly, with more hospitals and patients taking part. It was at the second such games in 1949 that Dr Guttmann famously said, "I foresaw the time when this sports event would be truly international and the Stoke Mandeville Games would achieve world fame as the disabled person's equivalent of the Olympic Games" (The Cord, 1949). In 1952 it became an international event for the first time with a team from the Netherlands competing. In 1953 a team from Canada joined. By 1954 there were also: Australians, Finns, Egyptians and Israelis.

In the late 1950s Dr Guttmann and others discussed the idea of holding the Stoke Mandeville Games outside the UK. As the Olympics were to be held in Rome, Dr Guttmann suggested that the

International Stoke Mandeville Games could be held there too. So, one week after the end of the Rome 1960 Olympic Games, 400 disabled athletes, representing 21 countries competed in nine events in the first overseas Stoke Mandeville Games for those with spinal cord injuries. This would later become known as the first Paralympic Games.

Initially, Dr Guttmann was adamant the Games would only be open to those with spinal cord injuries, but in 1976 two new classes were added: athletes with a visual impairment and athletes who were amputees. Over the next few games more classes were added to the six that there are today.

It was only in Seoul, Korea in 1988 that the Paralympic Games were held directly after the Olympic Summer Games, in the same host city, and using the same facilities. This set a precedent that was followed in 1992, 1996 and 2000. It was eventually formalised in an agreement between the International Paralympic Committee (IPC) and the International Olympic Committee (IOC) in 2001. The 1992 Winter Paralympics were the first Winter Games to use the same facilities as the Winter Olympics.

The Paralympic Games have come a long way from the first Stoke Mandeville Games, providing an opportunity for elite athletes with a disability to shine and inspire . The Paralympics continue to show in the words of Sir Philip Craven at the opening of the Sochi Winter Paralymics in 2014 "that what may not seem possible is possible."

1. This article is written to:
   a. Inform.
   b. Entertain.
   c. Warn.
   d. Gain sympathy for Paralympic athletes.

2. Which statement is true about the Paralympics?
   a. They have always followed the Olympics.
   b. They are a very new invention.
   c. They are always held in the U.K.
   d. They have grown to become an internationally acclaimed competition.

3. Dr Guttmann believed that:
   a. A person with a spinal injury had a pointless future.
   b. The Paralympics should be open to all.
   c. The Paralympics would always be a small competition.
   d. People could gain hope and self-worth through sport.

4. Which statement is true about the Paralympic Games?
   a. Bigger than the Olympic Games.
   b. Held every year.
   c. Held in Stoke Manderville.
   d. Started as an English event and then became international.

5. What does the author of the passage think about the Paralympic Games?
   a. The Paralympics are secondary to the Olympics.
   b. The Paralympians are great athletes but not at the level of those who compete at the Olympic Games.
   c. The Paralympians are elite athletes that show courage and skill.
   d. The view of the author is not shown in the passage.

Choose the correct work in the sentences below:

"Stop playing on the computer," said Mum. "You must [6](practice, practise, prey) the piano first. Then it will be time to [7](ate, eat, eight) dinner. I have [8](already, ready, soon) chopped all the vegetables and I am now sautéing the [9](meat, meet, moat). At dinner, I look forward to you telling me what you [10](done, did, worked) at school today."

In the questions below, all the words but one can be rearranged to make a sentence. Underline the extra word.

11. work   quickly   write   very   her   she   completed

12. she   and   milk   went   shops   to   to   the   buy

13. he   playing   games   on   computer   loved

14. and   friend   every   his   walked   too   day   school   to   Jack

15. exhausted   as   they   their   long   were   after   walk

Complete the antonym of the word in bold on the left.

16. **WORTHLESS**   p r e _ _ _ u s

17. **FAR**   c l _ _ _

18. **MEAN**   p l _ _ _ _ n t

19. **JOY**   s o _ _ _ w

20. **LONG**   b _ _ _ f

Read the excerpt from the story, "The Thief is the Dragon Rider" by Ruth Draper and answer the questions.

1 Verity kept trudging through the woods, the trees whispering, singing filled the air with little chirps
2 flittering tree to tree. Sheer mountains in the distance, the top sprinkled with snow, the icing on the
3 cake. Sunlight flickered through the trees looking like raindrops dancing on her feet; a sea of golden
4 flowers surrounded each tree. A singed tree lay ahead, barren land surrounding.
5
6 You hear stories of how there were five dragons in the kingdom each hunted for territory and
7 dominance - only one survived. Whether these stories are true or not depends on whose history
8 you believe: the humans or the elves. However the fact remains that if a dragon is threatened or his
9 territory was wanted he may be forced to help the humans in the battle. Verity felt more at ease
10 with this plan.
11
12 Dusk descending, Verity stumbled near the edge of the dragon's territory. Conflicting emotions
13 settled within her the top three fighting it out inside her stomach: fear, curiosity and excitement.
14 Walking through a break in the greenery, she was met with a mountain, the jagged rocks sprayed
15 erratically around to deter visitors. A cavity seemed to suck in all traces of light into its seemingly
16 bottomless pit.
17
18 As Verity peered into the darkness, a pair of large ruby eyes glared at her, holding ancient
19 knowledge watching from the shadows speaking into her mind.
20
21 "Who made the deliberate mistake to trespass on my domain?"
22 Mesmerised by the Ruby red dragon, silence echoed.
23 "Must I repeat myself or do you have any will of answering my question?"
24 Snapping out of her daze, Verity spoke "I am here to deliver a message from Panem to warn you,
25 that an unknown enemy has appeared at the borders of Panem, the army are proven to be
26 relentless and undaunted by their opposition, accompanied by a black dragon th"
27 Cut off quickly by the dragon, "say no more as I understand," he said, "you wish for me to slay the
28 dragon."
29
30 "Well, yes" plan now in tatters. Brilliant!
31 "What shall I receive for my service?"
32 The king never spoke of what should be done in return; she panicked as the dragon turned to walk
33 off. "What about a negotiation, what do you want in exchange for helping?" Verity asked.
34 "Not to send pitiful knights out to slay me; it grows old after the first millennium."

35 Trying to steady her racing heart she lies, "Yes, the king can do that."

36 "Then I vow to assist in the war, my name is Argento," he paused looking down at the human in

37 front of him "And you are my dragon rider."

1. This story is about:
   a. A quest to slay a dragon.
   b. A quest to get the dragon's service.
   c. A battle.
   d. The landscape of a place called Panem.

2. In line 4, the singed tree suggests:
   a. There were birds in the tree.
   b. It was spring.
   c. The tree had been burnt.
   d. The tree was a lovely shade of orange.

3. Which of the following types of literature does **not** describe the above story?
   a. Fictional.
   b. Historical.
   c. Descriptive.
   d. Mythical.

4. Where did the dragon live?
   a. In a cave.
   b. On the top of a mountain.
   c. On barren ground.
   d. In a tree.

5. What is the name of the dragon?
   a. Panem.
   b. Verity.
   c. Rose.
   d. Argento.

Choose the correct word in the passage below:

There is a saying that time [6](flew, fly, flies) when you are having fun. While there are still sixty minutes in an [7](our, hour, seconds), time does not seem to [8](pull, drag, fly) because it is easier to become [9](engrossed, captured, pedantic) in something that is enjoyable. Time also seems to go faster as people [10](are, is, become) older.

Choose the word which goes with both sets of brackets.

11. (quick, speed)   (fixed, firmly)   fast, swift, rapid, secure, tight

12. (heron, robin)   (tractor, excavator)   wren, eagle, kite, digger, crane

13. (fig, plum)   (month, day)   damson, prune, apple, date, year

14. (ascend, increased)   (daffodil, lily) height, upwards, daisy, rose, tulip

15. (twist, coil)   (injury, lesion)   wind, wound, spiral, bruise, sore

Complete the synonym of the words below:

16. **COURAGE**   V A _ _ _ R

17. **SHOW**   R E _ _ _ L

18. **UNCLEAR**   V A _ _ _

19. **HELP**   A S _ _ _ T

20. **ELEVATION**   A L _ _ _ _ D E

Read the poem "The Blind Men and the Elephant" by John Godfrey Saxe (1816-1887). Then answer
the questions below.

It was six men of Indostan,
To learning much inclined,
Who went to see the Elephant
(Though all of them were blind),
That each by observation
Might satisfy his mind.

The First approached the Elephant,
And happening to fall
Against his broad and sturdy side,
At once began to bawl:
"God bless me! but the Elephant
Is very like a WALL!"

The Second, feeling of the tusk,
Cried, "Ho, what have we here,
So very round and smooth and sharp?
To me 'tis mighty clear
This wonder of an Elephant
Is very like a SPEAR!"

The Third approached the animal,
And happening to take
The squirming trunk within his hands,
Thus boldly up and spake:
"I see," quoth he, "the Elephant
Is very like a SNAKE!"

The Fourth reached out an eager hand,
And felt about the knee
"What most this wondrous beast is like
Is mighty plain," quoth he:
"'Tis clear enough the Elephant
Is very like a TREE!"

The Fifth, who chanced to touch the ear,
Said: "E'en the blindest man
Can tell what this resembles most;
Deny the fact who can,
This marvel of an Elephant
Is very like a FAN!"

The Sixth no sooner had begun
About the beast to grope,
Than seizing on the swinging tail
That fell within his scope,
"I see," quoth he, "the Elephant
Is very like a ROPE!"

And so these men of Indostan
Disputed loud and long,
Each in his own opinion
Exceeding stiff and strong,
Though each was partly in the right,
And all were in the wrong!

1. How did the fourth blind man make an inference about the elephant when he touched one of its legs?
    a. He knew that trees grew in India.
    b. He knew that elephants were tall.
    c. He knew that trees were thick and rough and very tall.
    d. He knew that elephants were strong and didn't move.

2. What kind of story is this?
    a. Fable.
    b. Myth.
    c. Novel.
    d. Play.

3. Why did the blind men start to argue?
    a. Because they wanted to keep the elephant.
    b. Because they were confused.
    c. Because they were all wrong.
    d. Because each one thought his idea was the correct one.

4. What does the author mean when he says "Though each was partly in the right, and all were in the wrong?"
    a. He meant they were all right about what the elephant was.
    b. He meant the elephant was an animal but they were all wrong because they thought it was only things.
    c. He meant they were all wrong about what the elephant was.
    d. He meant they were all right about their guesses but they were all wrong because an elephant was not only a spear, or a rope, or a wall, etc.

5. What is the moral of the story?
    a. There are many different aspects to an elephant.
    b. If someone has a different perspective to me, it does not mean that they are wrong.
    c. People are all different and should be left to their own understanding.
    d. Blind people cannot "see" the whole picture.

Complete the words in the passage below:

The students had [6]comp _ _ _ _ d their [7]res _ _ _ _ h and were now writing it up. They

had looked up how the body stays warm in cold [8]temp _ _ _ _ ures. They had printed off at

least three [9]so _ _ _ _ s, which they now used to write a [10]re _ _ _ t.

Underline the word which is the odd one out.

11. bypass   follow   progress   farewell

12. weather   sleet   snow   hailstones

13. flaw   roar   fray   door

14. increase   ascend   rise   alter

15. orange   apple   lemon   mauve

Choose the word which is closest in meaning to the word on the left.

16. **ANXIOUS**   fear   nervous   miserable   courage

17. **FURIOUS**   upset   anger   irate   calm

18. **CRAVE**   crevice   cavity   hollow   yearn

19. **CURB**   limit   edge   path   road

20. **RESOLUTE**   answer   determined   decide   choice

Verbal Ability – Test 18

Read the excerpt from "Gulliver's Travels," by Dean Swift. Then answer the questions below.

1   Our histories of six thousand moons make no mention of any other regions than the two great
2   empires of Lilliput and Blefuscu. Which two mighty powers have, as I was going to tell you, been
3   engaged in a most obstinate war for six-and-thirty moons past. It began upon the following
4   occasion. It is allowed on all hands, that the primitive way of breaking eggs, before we eat them,
5   was upon the larger end; but his present majesty's grandfather, while he was a boy, going to eat an
6   egg, and breaking it according to the ancient practice, happened to cut one of his fingers.
7   Whereupon the emperor his father published an edict, commanding all his subjects, upon great
8   penalties, to break the smaller end of their eggs. The people so highly resented this law, that our
9   histories tell us, there have been six rebellions raised on that account; wherein one emperor lost his
10 life, and another his crown. These civil commotions were constantly fomented by the monarchs of
11 Blefuscu; and when they were quelled, the exiles always fled for refuge to that empire. It is
12 computed that eleven thousand persons have at several times suffered death, rather than submit to
13 break their eggs at the smaller end. Many hundred large volumes have been published upon this
14 controversy: but the books of the Big-endians have been long forbidden, and the whole party
15 rendered incapable by law of holding employments.

1. How long is their history?
   a. 3 years.
   b. 500 years.
   c. Six thousand years.
   d. The passage doesn't say.

2. What are the consequences of being a big-endian?
   a. You may not write about it.
   b. You cannot get a job.
   c. Possible death.
   d. All of the above.

3. Who made the law?
   a. The present king's son.
   b. The present king's father.
   c. The present king's grandfather.
   d. The present king's great-grandfather.

4. What word could be used to replace the word "fomented," in line 10?
    a. Stirred up.
    b. Started.
    c. Fermented.
    d. Halted.

5. What is the lesson from this story?
    a. Always crack your egg from the little end.
    b. Do not let little issues become big issues.
    c. Take note of the small things.
    d. Follow the laws that are made or your life could become very difficult.

Complete the words in the passage below:

Pizza is an [6]o _ _ _ - baked flat bread that is [7]t _ _ _ _ _ ionally topped with a tomato-based [8]sa _ _ _ and cheese as well as a [9]se _ _ _ _ ion of other toppings. The term first appeared in 997AD and pizza is still a [10]fa _ _ _ _ ite of many people today.

Underline the word which completes the analogies below.

11. July is to May as Wednesday is to	Sunday, Monday, Thursday, Friday
12. egg is to chicken as milk is to	carton, cheese, yoghurt, cow
13. way is to weigh as sew is to	sow, sour, so, sore
14. glass is to jug as pond is to	water, ocean, fish, bank
15. sand is to glass as cotton is to	plant, bud, fabric, bale

Underline the word which is most opposite in meaning to the word on the left.

16. hidden	concealed displayed covert obscured
17. reveal	cover divulge hide show
18. snubbed	ostracised offended respected welcomed
19. assert	claim deny reply request
20. tangible	abstract sensible reliable concrete

Read "The Fieldmouse" by Cecil Frances Alexander. Then answer the questions below.

1   Where the acorn tumbles down,
2   Where the ash tree sheds its berry,
3   With your fur so soft and brown,
4   With your eye so round and merry,
5   Scarcely moving the long grass,
6   Fieldmouse, I can see you pass.
7
8   Little thing, in what dark den,
9   Lie you all the winter sleeping?
10   Till warm weather comes again,
11   Then once more I see you peeping
12   Round about the tall tree roots,
13   Nibbling at their fallen fruits.
14
15   Fieldmouse, fieldmouse, do not go,
16   Where the farmer stacks his treasure,
17   Find the nut that falls below,
18   Eat the acorn at your pleasure,
19   But you must not steal the grain
20   He has stacked with so much pain.
21
22   Make your hole where mosses spring,
23   Underneath the tall oak's shadow,
24   Pretty, quiet harmless thing,
25   Play about the sunny meadow.
26   Keep away from corn and house,
27   None will harm you, little mouse.

1. What is the farmer's treasure?
   a. Money.
   b. Crops.
   c. Gold or minerals.
   d. Firewood.

2. From whose perspective is the poem written?
   a. The farmer.
   b. The mouse.
   c. First person.
   d. Third person.

3. In line 17 what does the nut refer to?
   a. An acorn.
   b. A peanut.
   c. A person.
   d. Some treasure.

4. What does the narrator think of mice?
   a. They're scary.
   b. They're a pest.
   c. They're inoffensive.
   d. They're nice.

5. What is the message of this poem?
   a. Mice hibernate in winter.
   b. The mouse is safe provided it stays in the natural habitat.
   c. The mouse needs to stay away from the farmer because he is evil.
   d. The mouse is a thief.

Choose the correct words in the passage below.

The word "flapjack" first [6](appear, appears, appeared) in the 1600s, even making an appearance in the play 'Pericles, Prince of Tyre', by William Shakespeare. However, the modern flapjack only [7](was, became, become) popular in the 1920s. Flapjacks are a thick slice made [8](from, by, some) oats, butter and golden syrup. There are many [9](variety, variations, variegated) of flapjacks. Besides the plain flapjack many have dried fruit or chocolate chips added. [10](Although, Since, However) in America, a "flapjack" is a pancake.

Choose the word that can go with both sets of brackets.

11. (allow, authorise) (ticket, pass)   permit, grant, licence, voucher, let

12. (cat, wolf) (carry, support)   endure, lion, giraffe, bear, uphold

13. (mark, stroke) (click, clack)   tap, beat, tick, tock, dash

14. (squash, soft drink) (hit, bash)   juice, water, blow, strike, punch

15. (robust, solid) (noise, echo)   secure, intact, stable, sturdy, sound

Complete the word to make a word that means the opposite or nearly the opposite of the word on the left.

16. advance   r e ▢ ▢ ▢ ▢ t

17. immaculate   f l ▢ ▢ ▢ d

18. abrasive   s ▢ ▢ ▢ h i n g

19. shaking   s t ▢ ▢ ▢ y

20. bored   e ▢ ▢ ▢ t e d

Verbal Ability – Test 20

Read the story of *Dick Whittington and his Cat*. Then answer the questions below.

There was a little boy called Dick Whittington, whose father and mother died. As poor Dick was not old enough to work, he was very badly off – for the people who lived in the village were very poor, and could not spare him much more than the parings of potatoes. Dick walked to London to seek his fortune.

Once in London, finding nothing but dirt, Dick sat down in a dark corner and cried himself to sleep. After a time, being almost starved, he laid himself down at the door of Mr Fitzwarren, a rich merchant. When Mr Fitzwarren himself came home to dinner, and saw a dirty, ragged boy lying at the door, he said to him, "Why do you lie there, my boy? You seem old enough to work. I am afraid you are inclined to be lazy." "No indeed, sir," said Dick to him, "that is not the case – for I would work, but I do not know anybody. I believe I am very sick for the want of food." So the kind merchant ordered him to be taken into the house, have a good dinner, and be kept to do what work he was able to do for the cook.

Little Dick would have lived very happily in this good family, if it had not been for the ill-natured cook. She used to say, "You are under me, so clean the spit and the dripping-pan, make the fires, wind up the jack, and do all the scullery work nimbly, or –" and she would shake the ladle at him.

Besides this, Dick's bed stood in a small garret, where every night he was tormented with rats and mice. A gentleman had given Dick a penny for cleaning his shoes, so he bought a cat with it. Dick cared well for his cat and had no more trouble with the rats and mice, but slept soundly every night.

Later, his master had a ship ready to sail; and as it was the custom that all his servants should have some chance for good fortune as well as himself, he called them all into the parlour and asked them what they would send out. When poor Dick heard this, he said, "I have nothing but a cat." Dick went upstairs and brought down poor puss, with tears in his eyes, and gave her to the captain.

At last poor Dick could not bear his treatment by the cook any longer, and thought he would run away. He walked as far as Holloway; and there he sat down on a stone. While he was thinking what he should do, the bells of Bow Church, began to ring, and at their sound seemed to say to him:

"Turn again, Whittington,
Thrice Lord Mayor of London."

"Lord Mayor of London!" said he to himself. "I would put up with almost anything now, to be Lord Mayor!" Dick went back, and was lucky enough to set about his work before the cook came downstairs.

We must now follow Miss Puss to the coast of Africa. The ship was at last driven by the winds to a part of the coast of Barbary; where the only people were the Moors, unknown to the English. The people came in great numbers to see the sailors, treated them civilly and were very eager to buy the fine things with which the ship was loaded. When the captain saw this, he sent samples of the best things he had to the king of the country; who was so pleased that he sent for the captain to the palace. They had not been sat long, when a vast number of rats and mice rushed in and devoured all the meat in an instant. The captain asked if these vermin were not unpleasant.

"Oh, yes," said they, "very offensive; and the king would give half his treasure to be freed of them. The captain told the king he had a creature on board the ship that would dispatch all these vermin immediately. The king jumped high at the joy the news gave him. "Bring this creature to me," said he, "if she will perform what you say, I will load your ship with gold and jewels in exchange for her."

Away went the captain to the ship, while another dinner was made. He arrived back at the palace just in time to see the table full of rats. The cat jumped out of the captain's arms, and in a few minutes laid most of the rats and mice dead at her feet. The rest in their fright scampered to their holes. The king, having seen the exploits of Miss Puss, bargained with the captain for the whole ship's cargo, and then gave him ten times as much for the cat as all the rest amounted to. The captain then took leave of the royal party, and set sail for England, and after a happy voyage arrived safe in London.

Early one morning, Mr Fitzwarren had just seated himself at his desk, when somebody came tap-tapping at the door. Mr Fitzwarren asked who it was. "A friend; I come to bring you good news of your ship, *Unicorn*." They then told the story of the cat. As soon as the merchant heard this, he called out to his servants, to go and fetch Dick. Mr Fitzwarren showed himself to be a good man; for when some of his servants said the treasure was too much for him, answered, "I will not deprive him of a single penny," even though it now made Dick even richer than himself. Mr Fitzwarren then told the men to open the great treasure. Dick was filled with joy. He begged his master to take what part of it he pleased. "No, no," answered Mr Fitzwarren, "this is all your own; and I have no doubt you will use it well."

Dick next asked his mistress, and then Miss Alice, the merchant's daughter to accept a part of his good fortune. The declined but told him they felt great joy at his good success. Mr Fitzwarren advised him to send for a proper tailor. When Whittington's face was washed, his hair curled, his hat cocked, and he was dressed in a nice suit, he was as handsome and genteel as any young man who visited. Miss Alice, who had been so kind to him, now looked upon him as fit to be her sweetheart; and the more so, no doubt, because Whittington was now always thinking what he could do to oblige her, and making her the prettiest presents that could be.Mr Fitzwarren soon saw their love for each other, and proposed to join them in marriage; and to this they both readily agreed. A day for the wedding was soon fixed; and they were attended to church by the Lord Mayor, and a great number of the richest merchants in London, whom they treated to a very rich feast.

History tells us that Mr Whittington and his lady lived in great splendour, and were very happy. They had several children. Whittington was seen as a good and kind man. Whittington's acts of charity include building a college, a church and Newgate Prison. He was thrice Lord Mayor, and received the honour of knighthood by Henry V.

1. Why did Dick go to London?
   a. To become famous.
   b. To become rich.
   c. To get a cat.
   d. He hoped to be Lord Mayor of London.

2. What described the place that Dick slept in Mr Fitzwarren's house?
   a. In a cold and damp basement.
   b. On the floor of the kitchen.
   c. In the attic.
   d. In an airy bedroom.

3. What time was it that Dick ran away and heard the bells of Bow Church?
   a. Early morning.
   b. Mid-morning.
   c. Noon.
   d. The passage doesn't say

4. Why did Dick decide to run away?
   a. He missed the cat.
   b. The cook was unkind to him.
   c. Mr Fitzwarren fired him.
   d. He heard the bells speak to him.

5. In the story Mr Fitzwarren is a merchant. What does merchant mean?
   a. A rich man who lives in a big house.
   b. A mayor.
   c. Someone who has a ship.
   d. Someone who buys and sells goods to make money.

Complete the words in the passage below.

The West End is an area of [6]Cen _ _ _ l London, containing many of the city's major

[7]to _ _ _ st attractions, including the well known West End [8]The _ _ _ _ s. The shows in the

West End are normally considered to be the best in the English [9]sp _ _ _ ing world. West End

shows are enjoyed by over twelve [10]mi _ _ _ _ n people every year.

Underline the two words which should swap places in the sentences below.

    11. He very the party left early.

    12. He was stopped for the police by speeding.

    13. The fence down came in the storm.

    14. You should your put always rubbish in the bin.

    15. He always did a healthy diet and ate lots of exercise.

Complete the word to make a word that means the opposite or nearly the opposite of the word on the left.

    16. artificial   n a t _ _ _ l

    17. tiny   e n o r _ _ _ _

    18. agree   c o n t r _ _ _ _ _ t

    19. belittle   _ _ _ t t e r

    20. aware   i g n _ _ _ _ t

Verbal Ability – Test 21

Read the passage below about carrots and then answer the questions.

1 The carrot is a type of vegetable, usually orange in colour, though purple, red, white, and yellow
2 varieties exist. The part that is most commonly eaten is actually the tap root. The domestic carrot
3 has been selectively bred for its greatly enlarged and more palatable, less woody-textured edible
4 taproot.
5
6 The wild ancestors of the carrot probably came from Persia (regions of which are now Iran and
7 Afghanistan). When they were first cultivated, carrots were grown for their aromatic leaves and
8 seeds rather than their roots. Some close relatives of the carrot are still grown for their leaves and
9 seeds, for example parsley, fennel, dill and cumin. Carrot seeds have been found in Switzerland and
10 Southern Germany dating to 2000–3000 BC. Orange coloured carrots first appeared in the
11 Netherlands in the 17th century, sometimes thought to be due to the House of Orange, the Dutch
12 royalty. Prior to the orange carrot the most common colour of carrots was white, purple or later
13 yellow. Purple carrots, still orange on the inside, were sold in British stores starting in 2002.
14
15 The distinctive orange colour of our familiar modern carrot is due to the presence of β-carotene
16 (pronounced beta-carotene). β-carotene also found in other vegetables such as pumpkin and sweet
17 potato is a precursor to vitamin A. Vitamin A plays an important role in vision, bone growth and
18 health of the immune system. Vitamin A also helps the surface of the eye, mucous membranes and
19 skin be effective barriers to bacteria and viruses, reducing the risk of eye infections, respiratory
20 problems and other infectious diseases.
21
22 Carrots have long been seen as a nutritious addition to our diet. They can be eaten in a myriad of
23 ways. Carrots can be eaten either raw or cooked. They are a ubiquitous salad ingredient and one of
24 the two main ingredients of coleslaw. They are also baked, fried with butter and honey to make
25 'honey carrots,' or put into a stew. While most foods containing carrots are savoury, carrot cake and
26 carrot muffins are also popular.

1. What type of vegetable is the carrot?
    a. Woody vegetable.
    b. Root vegetable.
    c. Fruity vegetable.
    d. Orange vegetable

2. Which statement about carrots is definitely true?
    a. All carrots are orange.
    b. Carrots became orange to commemorate the House of Orange in the Netherlands.
    c. Carrots are important for eyesight.
    d. Carrots contain vitamin A.

3. What word could be used to replace 'ubiquitious' in line 23?
    a. Everywhere.
    b. Excellent.
    c. Crisp.
    d. Common.

4. What type of word is savoury in line 25?
    a. Noun.
    b. Verb.
    c. Adjective.
    d. Adverb.

5. What is the carrot related most closely to?
    a. Parsley.
    b. Sweet potato and pumpkin.
    c. Tomato.
    d. Oranges.

Choose the correct words in the passage below.

Comics are a [6](strip, medium, art) used to express ideas with images, often combined with [7](printing, wording, text). Comics therefore are a type of [8](frieze, freeze, warmth). Comics often take the form of sequences of images. Some comics are written for fun and contain humour while others try and [9](demonstrate, portray, write) a message or try to persuade people of an idea. One of the more popular [10](type, typing, types) of comic is the Japanese manga.

In each of the questions below. All the words except one can be made into a sentence. Underline the word that is not used.

11. the milk sell ran shop had of out

12. new forward they their moving looked to into move house

13. asked teacher the to quiet student them be

14. World Book Day character for his dressed as he favourite enjoyed

15. accident car she tree the hit when damaged the she

Choose the synonym of the word on the right

16. **HUGE**   immense, intense, miniscule, high, large

17. **ABOLISH**   allow, build, restrain, cancel, inhibit

18. **LENIENT**   slant, strong, compliant, slow, lazy

19. **RAVENOUS**   ruby, starving, satisfied, flying, lofty

20. **EXTEND**   massive, shorten, pursue, continue, copious

Verbal Ability – Test 22

Read the passage below from "Hard Times" by Charles Dickens and then answer the questions.

1 'NOW, what I want is, Facts. Teach these boys and girls nothing but Facts. Facts alone are wanted
2 in life. Plant nothing else, and root out everything else. You can only form the minds of reasoning
3 animals upon Facts: nothing else will ever be of any service to them. This is the principle on which I
4 bring up my own children, and this is the principle on which I bring up these children. Stick to Facts,
5 sir!'

6
7 The scene was a plain, bare, monotonous vault of a school-room, and the speaker's square
8 forefinger emphasized his observations by underscoring every sentence with a line on the
9 schoolmaster's sleeve. The emphasis was helped by the speaker's square wall of a forehead, which
10 had his eyebrows for its base, while his eyes found commodious cellarage in two dark caves,
11 overshadowed by the wall. The emphasis was helped by the speaker's mouth, which was wide,
12 thin, and hard set. The emphasis was helped by the speaker's voice, which was inflexible, dry, and
13 dictatorial. The emphasis was helped by the speaker's hair, which bristled on the skirts of his bald
14 head, a plantation of firs to keep the wind from its shining surface, all covered with knobs, like the
15 crust of a plum pie, as if the head had scarcely warehouse-room for the hard facts stored inside.
16 The speaker's obstinate carriage, square coat, square legs, square shoulders,—nay, his very
17 neckcloth, trained to take him by the throat with an unaccommodating grasp, like a stubborn fact,
18 as it was,—all helped the emphasis.
19
20 'In this life, we want nothing but Facts, sir; nothing but Facts!'
21
22 The speaker, and the schoolmaster, and the third grown person present, all backed a little, and
23 swept with their eyes the inclined plane of little vessels then and there arranged in order, ready to
24 have imperial gallons of facts poured into them until they were full to the brim.

1. What did the classroom have on its walls?
    a. Facts.
    b. Posters.
    c. Students' work.
    d. Nothing.

2. What are the little vessels mentioned in line 23?
    a. Exercise books.
    b. Containers.
    c. Children.
    d. Cannot tell from the passage.

3. What type of word is the word principle is lines 3 and 4?
    a. Noun.
    b. Verb.
    c. Adjective.
    d. Adverb.

4. In line 2 the phrase "Plant nothing else, and root out everything else." is an example of what type of literary device?
    a. Metaphor.
    b. Simile.
    c. Personification.
    d. Alliteration.

5. What was the speaker wearing?
    a. Skirt.
    b. Coat and tie.
    c. Jeans.
    d. Not told in the passage.

Choose the correct words in the passage below.

The rocket was launched from the [6](runway, harbour, pad) at
[7](November, Friday, 11 o'clock). The booster engines converted the
huge tanks of fuel into gases by combustion. The gases shot out the base
of the rocket [8](send, propelling, escaping) the rocket in the opposite
direction. The engines were then discarded making the rocket lighter.
The discarded rocket sections quickly [9](burn, burnt, burns) up in the
atmosphere. Initially taking off vertically, the rocket needed to reach a speed of 28 000 km/h
before entering [10](orbit, cosmos, the moon). A successful launch, now it time to head home for
dinner.

In each of the questions below. All the words except one can be made into a sentence. Underline
the word that is not used.

11. still was asked more hungry for drink he and

12. thirty children made ago or to rode walked school most years

13. was star the the drama theatre in actor to chosen new

14. see favourite to play booked she her team tickets act

15. changed years lot the had a in area recent was local

Complete the synonym of the word on the right

16. **ARGUE**   q u _ _ _ e l

17. **STAY**   r _ _ _ _ n

18. **CLIMB**   a _ _ _ n d

19. **NORMAL**   u s _ _ l

20. **HIDE**   c o n c _ _ _

Read "How Brother Rabbit Fooled the Whale and the Elephant" by Sara Cone Bryant and then answer the questions.

1 One day little Brother Rabbit was running along on the sand, lippety, lippety, when he saw the
2 Whale and the Elephant talking together. Little Brother Rabbit crouched down and listened to what
3 they were saying. This was what they were saying:--

4 "You are the biggest thing on the land, Brother Elephant," said the Whale, "and I am the biggest
5 thing in the sea; if we join together we can rule all the animals in the world, and have our way about
6 everything."

7 "Very good, very good," trumpeted the Elephant; "that suits me; we will do it."

8 Little Brother Rabbit snickered to himself. "They won't rule me," he said. He ran away and got a very
9 long, very strong rope, and he got his big drum, and hid the drum a long way off in the bushes. Then
10 he went along the beach till he came to the Whale.

11 "Oh, please, dear, strong Mr. Whale," he said, "will you have the great kindness to do me a favour?
12 My cow is stuck in the mud, a quarter of a mile from here. And I can't pull her out. But you are so
13 strong and so obliging, that I venture to trust you will help me out."

14 The Whale was so pleased with the compliment that he said, "Yes," at once. "Then," said the
15 Rabbit, "I will tie this end of my long rope to you, and I will run away and tie the other end round my
16 cow, and when I am ready I will beat my big drum. When you hear that, pull very, very hard, for the
17 cow is stuck very deep in the mud."

18 "Huh!" grunted the Whale, "I'll pull her out, if she is stuck to the horns."

19 Little Brother Rabbit tied the rope-end to the whale, and ran off, lippety, lippety, till he came to the
20 place where the Elephant was.

21 "Oh, please, mighty and kindly Elephant," he said, making a very low bow "will you do me a favour?"

22 "What is it?" asked the Elephant.

23 "My cow is stuck in the mud, about a quarter of a mile from here," said little Brother Rabbit, "and I
24 cannot pull her out. Of course you could. If you will be so very obliging as to help me--"

25 "Certainly," said the Elephant grandly,

26 "Certainly."

27 "Then," said little Brother Rabbit, "I will tie one end of this long rope to your trunk, and the other to
28 my cow, and as soon as I have tied her tightly I will beat my big drum. When you hear that, pull; pull
29 as hard as you can, for my cow is very heavy."

30 "Never fear," said the Elephant, "I could pull twenty cows."

31 "I am sure you could," said the Rabbit, politely, "only be sure to begin gently, and pull harder and
32 harder till you get her."

33 Then he tied the end of the rope tightly round the Elephant's trunk, and ran away into the bushes.
34 There he sat down and beat the big drum.

35 The Whale began to pull, and the Elephant began to pull, and in a jiffy the rope tightened till it was
36 stretched as hard as could be.

37 "This is a remarkably heavy cow," said the Elephant; "but I'll fetch her!" And he braced his forefeet
38 in the earth, and gave a tremendous pull.

39 "Dear me!" said the Whale. "That cow must be stuck mighty tight;" and he drove his tail deep in the
40 water, and gave a marvellous pull.

41 He pulled harder; the Elephant pulled harder. Pretty soon the Whale found himself sliding toward
42 the land. The reason was, of course, that the Elephant had something solid to brace against, and,
43 too, as fast as he pulled the rope in a little, he took a turn with it round his trunk!

44 But when the Whale found himself sliding toward the land he was so provoked with the cow that he
45 dove head first, down to the bottom of the sea. That was a pull! The Elephant was jerked off his
46 feet, and came slipping and sliding to the beach, and into the surf. He was terribly angry. He braced
47 himself with all his might, and pulled his best. At the jerk, up came the Whale out of the water.

48 "Who is pulling me?" spouted the Whale.

49 "Who is pulling me?" trumpeted the Elephant.

50 And then each saw the rope in the other's hold.

51 "I'll teach you to play cow!" roared the Elephant.

52 "I'll show you how to fool me!" fumed the Whale. And they began to pull again. But this time the
53 rope broke, the Whale turned a somersault, and the Elephant fell over backwards.

54 At that, they were both so ashamed that neither would speak to the other. So that broke up the
55 bargain between them.

56 And little Brother Rabbit sat in the bushes and laughed, and laughed, and laughed.

1. What type of writing is this?
   a. Biography.
   b. Reporting.
   c. Narrative.
   d. Parody.

2. In this story the rabbit speaks. This is an example of:
   a. Personification.
   b. Alliteration.
   c. Assonance.
   d. Metaphor.

3. What word could be used to describe the rabbit?
   a. Proud.
   b. Honest.
   c. Crafty.
   d. Stubborn.

4. What kept the whale and the elephant pulling?
   a. Insolence.
   b. The rabbit hadn't told them they could let go.
   c. Strength.
   d. Pride.

5. What did rabbit use to get the whale and the elephant to pull?
   a. Cheek.
   b. Flattery.
   c. Cute and feeble.
   d. Charisma.

Choose the correct words in the passage below.

It would [6](of, have, is) been an [7](great, miserable, excellent) day. The sun [8](shone, shined, shining) brightly in the sky and the birds [9](sang, flit, fly) from tree to tree. If only I was able to be [10](in, their, out) and enjoy it.

In each of the questions below, choose the word on the left that goes equally with both pairs of brackets.

11. (dollar, pence, yen) (punch, wrestle, box)   rumble, cents, pound, euro, fight

12. (spin, turn, sprint) (loaf, bread, croissant)   run, jump, hop, skip, roll

13. (quick, speed, rapid) (tight, firm, secure)   fast, slick, swift, brisk, firm

14. (leave, abandon, trap)   (red, burgundy, cerise)   strand, forsake, isolate, crimson, maroon

15. (lump, heap, pile) (weight, size, length)   density, magnitude, mass, capacity, bulk

Choose the antonym of the word on the right

16. **UNFRIENDLY**   a m _ _ _ l e

17. **ORDER**   t u r _ _ _ l

18. **GENUINE**   i m i _ _ _ i o n

19. **LEND**   b o _ _ _ w

20. **FAILED**   p a _ _ _ d

Verbal Ability Test 24

28-11-1987

There was a black-out last week at the hospital, as the hospital generator failed. This was not a major issue during the day but at night it was a problem navigating around the dogs in order to get to the patients. Unfortunately one nurse tripped over a goat and badly sprained her ankle. Life here continues to be filled with unusual challenges.

1. Why did the hospital have no electricity?
   a. Electricity had not yet been invented.
   b. The hospital generator had stopped working.
   c. Hospitals don't use electricity.
   d. A goat had gnawed through a cable.

2. Which was the **main** problem caused by the lack of electricity?
   a. The animals could not be seen.
   b. The hospital medical equipment needs electricity.
   c. Some patients are afraid of the dark.
   d. The computers don't work so they don't know what patients are in the hospital.

3. What type of word is navigating?
   a. Noun
   b. Verb
   c. Adjective
   d. Adverb

4. Why did the writer describe the situation as an unusual challenge?
   a. Equipment does not normally fail.
   b. It's hard to work with a sprained ankle.
   c. Navigation is always a challenge.
   d. This would not happen in a hospital in England.

5. What type of prose is this passage?
   a. Biography
   b. Letter
   c. Journal
   d. Informative

Choose the correct word in the passage below:

The internet has completely [6](subdued, generic, transformed, increased) the way we

communicate. No longer are we limited to contacting one person at a time but with the

[7](concept, advent, appeal, reminiscence) of social media sites such as Facebook people can be

informed of news [8](simultaneously, redundant, combined, repeating). Further, news can be

sent internationally very quickly. This means that when the arrival of a new baby is [9](shown,

joyous, said, announced) in England, the first [10](gratitude commendation, interjection,

congratulations) may come from as far away as Tanzania.

In each question below, all the words except one can be rearranged to make a sentence.

Choose the word which is not needed to make the sentence.

11. bus caught always driver the same to school she

12. Sports' Day long for on broke student athletics jump the the record

13. he camping holidays tent was going Summer during his

14. the Earth shorter than days Winter Summer are in

15. homework television finish must you you your run watch before

Choose the synonym to the words below:

16. **BEGINNER**   avid sad novice commence

17. **INDULGENT**   lenient judgemental acrid hostile

18. **SHARE**   order choose potion dole

19. **DETERMINED**   honourable esteemed defeated adamant

20. **EXCEED**   depth height surpass accumulate

Read the adapted opening passage of *The Lost Prince* by Frances Hodgson Burnett, then answer the questions below.

There are many dreary and dingy rows of ugly houses in certain parts of London, but there certainly could not be any row more ugly or dingier than Philibert Place. There were stories that it had once been more attractive, but that had been so long ago that no one remembered the time. It stood back in its gloomy, narrow strips of uncared-for, smoky gardens, whose broken iron railings were supposed to protect it from the surging traffic of a road which was always roaring with the rattle of busses, cabs, drays, and vans, and the passing of people who were shabbily dressed and looked as if they were either going to hard work or coming from it, or hurrying to see if they could find some of it to do to keep themselves from going hungry. The brick fronts of the houses were blackened with smoke, their windows were nearly all dirty and hung with dingy curtains, or had no curtains at all; the strips of ground, which had once been intended to grow flowers in, had been trodden down into bare earth in which even weeds had forgotten to grow. One of them was used as a stone-cutter's yard, and cheap monuments, crosses, and slates were set out for sale, bearing inscriptions beginning with "Sacred to the Memory of." Another had piles of old lumber in it, another exhibited second-hand furniture, chairs with unsteady legs, sofas with horsehair stuffing bulging out of holes in their covering, mirrors with blotches or cracks in them. The insides of the houses were as gloomy as the outside. They were all exactly alike. In each a dark entrance passage led to narrow stairs going up to bedrooms, and to narrow steps going down to a basement kitchen. The back bedroom looked out on small, sooty, flagged yards, where thin cats quarrelled, or sat on the coping of the brick walls hoping that sometime they might feel the sun; the front rooms looked over the noisy road, and through their windows came the roar and rattle of it. It was shabby and cheerless on the brightest days, and on foggy or rainy ones it was the most forlorn place in London.

At least that was what one boy thought as he stood near the iron railings watching the passers-by on the morning on which this story begins, which was also the morning after he had been brought by his father to live as a lodger in the back sitting-room of the house No. 7.

He was a boy about twelve years old, his name was Marco Loristan, and he was the kind of boy people look at a second time when they have looked at him once. In the first place, he was a very big boy—tall for his years, and with a particularly strong frame. His shoulders were broad and his arms and legs were long and powerful. He was quite used to hearing people say, as they glanced at him, "What a fine, big lad!" And then they always looked again at his face. His features were strong, his black hair grew on his head like a mat, his eyes were large and deep set, and looked out between thick, straight, black lashes. He was as un-English a boy as one could imagine, and an observing person would have been struck at once by a sort of SILENT look expressed by his whole face, a look which suggested that he was not a boy who talked much.

This look was especially noticeable this morning as he stood before the iron railings. The things he was thinking of were of a kind likely to bring to the face of a twelve-year-old boy an unboyish expression.

He was thinking of the long, hurried journey he and his father and their old soldier servant, Lazarus, had made during the last few days—the journey from Russia. Cramped in a close third-class railway carriage, they had dashed across the Continent as if something important or terrible were driving them, and here they were, settled in London as if they were going to live forever at No. 7 Philibert Place. He knew, however, that though they might stay a year, it was just as probable that, in the middle of some night, his father or Lazarus might waken him from his sleep and say, "Get up—dress yourself quickly. We must go at once." A few days later, he might be in St. Petersburg, Berlin, Vienna, or Budapest, huddled away in some poor little house as shabby and comfortless as No. 7 Philibert Place.

He passed his hand over his forehead as he thought of it and watched the busses. His strange life and his close association with his father had made him much older than his years, but he was only a boy, after all, and the mystery of things sometimes weighed heavily upon him, and set him to deep wondering.

In not one of the many countries he knew had he ever met a boy whose life was in the least like his own. Other boys had homes in which they spent year after year; they went to school regularly, and played with other boys, and talked openly of the things which happened to them, and the journeys they made. When he remained in a place long enough to make a few boy-friends, he knew he must never forget that his whole existence was a sort of secret whose safety depended upon his own silence and discretion.

This was because of the promises he had made to his father, and they had been the first thing he remembered. Not that he had ever regretted anything connected with his father. He threw his head up as he thought of that. None of the other boys had such a father, not one of them. His father was his idol and his chief. He had scarcely ever seen him when his clothes had not been poor and shabby, but he had also never seen him when, despite his worn coat and frayed linen, he had not stood out among all others as more distinguished than the most noticeable of them. When he walked down a street, people turned to look at him even oftener than they turned to look at Marco, and the boy felt as if it was not merely because he was a big man with a handsome, dark face, but because he looked, somehow, as if he had been born to command armies, and as if no one would think of disobeying him. Yet Marco had never seen him command any one, and they had always been poor, and shabbily dressed, and often enough ill-fed. But whether they were in one country or another, and whatsoever dark place they seemed to be hiding in, the few people they saw treated him with a sort of deference, and nearly always stood when they were in his presence, unless he bade them sit down.

He himself wished to be a patriot, though he had never seen his own country of Samavia. He knew it well, however.

1. Where had Marco travelled to London from?
   a. London.
   b. Russia.
   c. Samavia.
   d. Africa.

2. How did travelling constantly from place to place make Marco feel?
   a. Miserable.
   b. Frightened.
   c. Cramped.
   d. Unsettled.

3. When describing Philbert Place what does the author mean by "even weeds had forgotten to grow"?
   a. Everything was forgetful.
   b. Everything is dismal.
   c. The road is abandoned.
   d. Everything was very quiet.

4. How are Marco and his father portrayed in this passage?
   a. Poor.
   b. Middle class.
   c. Wealthy.
   d. Soldiers.

5. Why does the passage suggest that Marco does not talk much?
   a. He had only just arrived in England, so can't speak English.
   b. His life was very different to the other boys.
   c. He had to keep things a secret.
   d. He was shy.

Cloze

Fill in the missing letters in the passage below.

The ship was now fully [6]l _ _ _ ed with its cargo. The ship was filled to

[7]cap _ _ _ _ y to maximise [8]pr _ _ _ ts. The sailors [9]b _ _ _ ded the ship, raised the

mast and set sail for [10]th _ _ _ destination.

Locate the punctuation errors in the passage below. If there are no mistakes choose the N on the right.

11. The horse galloped, quickly over the fields towards home.

A	B	C	D

N

12. It had been a pleasant journey but horse and rider were glad to be

A	B	C	D

N

13. back in familiar territory. They had visited York Leeds and Haworth.

A	B	C	D

N

14. They had covered many miles every day often over difficult terrain.

A	B	C	D

N

15. "Well after that long trip we have earned our rest" said the rider.

A	B	C	D

N

Choose the antonym of the word on the left.

5.   poor   dejected, destitute, affluent, influential

7.   intentional   logical, rational, silly, accidental

8.   dilapidated   pristine, sparkling, old, modern

9.   broad   elegant, fine, cramped, trim

10.   impossible   probable, likely, certain, always

Read the following passage about trains and then answer the questions.

The train is a form of transport. The earliest trains used horses or bulls to pull carriages along simple train tracks. This allowed the animals to pull with less force than if their cargo was not on a rail. However, it was the steam train from the turn of the 19th century which would transform Britain and other places around the globe. The iconic sound of the steam engine and the black smoke from the burnt coal quickly became an everyday reality.

The steam train transformed the British landscape, enabling the Industrial Revolution to occur. The steam train made it possible for materials to be transported quickly and away from the canal network. This further led to the urbanisation of Britain, as the Industrial Revolution opened up new jobs. In 1801, before the advent of the steam engine, London was home to 864,845 people, according to the census, whilst in 1851 it had nearly tripled to 2,362,236. This changed the fabric of society as small tight-knit agricultural communities gave way as the most prevalent form of British society.

One of the characteristics of the steam engine, was the smoke billowing from the chimney. Polluted rivers and smoke-filled air began to dominate cities, dramatically changing the landscape. The burning of coal meant large amounts of carbon dioxide were emitted resulting in poor air quality.

Rail was much faster than the current transport methods and opened up Britain in a way that coach and barge could not do. Seaside fishing villages became fashionable and popular as day trips, holiday destinations and as cures for one's health. Towns and cities had cheaper food as farmers could get their perishable products to market quicker and cheaper. Inland towns could even get fresh seafood.

Steam's end finally came in 1968, for all but a few novelty tracks, as electrification and diesel became the standard for train transport. Electric trains could be powered by overhead wires or additional rails.

Just as Britain was the birthplace of the steam engine, it was to become the birthplace of another milestone in the history of the locomotive: that of the maglev train. Maglev stands for magnetic levitation. The maglev train uses magnets to lift the train above the modified rail called a guideway and propel it forward. As the train is lifted above the guideway, there is very little friction resulting in the high speeds produced in maglev trains.

Trains continue to be a common form of transport for both passengers and cargo. While many people use trains for short distances to commute to work, the longest passenger rail service running between two cities without changing takes passengers over 10000 km of terrain in nearly 9 days, between Russia and Korea.

1. What is the type of fuel used in steam engines?
    a. Coal.
    b. Carbon dioxide.
    c. Steam.
    d. Diesel.

2. What does the author think about trains?
    a. That they are wonderful as they allowed technological progress.
    b. Dislikes them as they are dirty.
    c. That they have changed the very nature of British society.
    d. That they keep changing so prevent stability.

3. According to the passage which of the following is an advantage of the train?
    a. Release carbon dioxide.
    b. Look majestic.
    c. Led to the urbanisation of London.
    d. Food became cheaper.

4. What could be used to replace "tight-knit" at the end of the second paragraph?
    a. Woollen.
    b. Supportive.
    c. Rural.
    d. Gathered.

5. The words "fabric of society" at the end of the second paragraph is an example of:
    a. Simile.
    b. Metaphor.
    c. Alliteration.
    d. Assonance.

Choose the correct word in the passage below.

Traditional power stations [6](manipulate, transform, generate) the energy found in oil or coal [7](in, into, on) electrical energy. It does this by spinning a magnet between coils of wire. This makes an electric [8](current, currant, raisin) flow [9](through, over, though) the wire. In some power stations renewable forms of energy [10](through which, because of, such as) wind can turn the magnet.

In the questions below, choose the word on the right that goes equally with both sets of brackets.

11. (acts, did) (ewes, mares)   does, went, plays, vixen, sows

12. (guide, conduct) (copper, sodium)   marshal, lead, shepherd, head, silver

13. (leaf, trunk) (miaow, growl)   bark, sap, branch, chirp, bleat

14. (parsley, thyme) (new, pristine)   fresh, perfect, basil, mint, rosemary

15. (remainder, residue) (relax, nap)   remnant, left-over, recline, ease, rest

Choose the word, which is a synonym of the word on the left.

16. **GLASSES**   opticians, tumblers, crystal, drink, mirror

17. **SINK**   boat, sea, basin, bay, hull

18. **GLISTENED**   beam, glance, oily, hear, shimmer

19. **WHIRLWIND**   sluggish, fast, lightning, fuss, blow

20. **SEETHE**   calm, sorrow, angry, appease, quieten

Read the following passage on the life of Alexander Fleming and the answer the questions below.

Alexander Fleming was born in Ayrshire, Scotland in 1881. As a boy, Fleming worked in a shipping office in London until, at the age of 22, an inheritance from his uncle enabled him to study medicine at St Mary's Hospital. He qualified with distinction as a doctor, in 1906. While at the medical school Fleming had been an active member of the rifle club. The captain of the club, wishing to retain Fleming in the team suggested that he join the research department at St Mary's. So, he became assistant bacteriologist to Sir Almroth Wright, a pioneer in vaccine therapy and immunology. In 1908, he was awarded a Bachelor of Science degree with Gold Medal in Bacteriology. Fleming then became a lecturer at St Mary's until 1914.

Fleming served throughout World War I as a captain in the Royal Army Medical Corps. He and many of his colleagues worked in war hospitals. In 1918 he returned to St Mary's Hospital, where he was elected Professor of Bacteriology of the University of London in 1928. He was to be elected Emeritus Professor of Bacteriology at the University of London in 1948. He was elected fellow of the Royal Society in 1943 and knighted in 1944.

By 1927, Fleming had been investigating the properties of a bacteria called *staphylococci*. He had developed a reputation as a brilliant researcher, but his laboratory was often untidy. In September 1928, Fleming returned to his laboratory having spent August on holiday with his family. Before leaving he had stacked all his plates of bacteria on a bench in a corner of his laboratory. He noticed a halo of inhibition of bacterial growth around a contaminant blue-green mould on one of the plates. He concluded that the mould was releasing a substance that was inhibiting bacterial growth. He grew a pure culture of the mould and discovered that it was *Penicillium notatum*. With help from a chemist, he concentrated what he later named "penicillin".

In Oxford, Ernst Boris Chain and Edward Abraham discovered how to isolate and concentrate penicillin. In 1945 Fleming, Florey and Chain shared the Nobel Prize in Medicine.

He later said of the discovery, "When I woke up just after dawn on September 28, 1928, I certainly didn't plan to revolutionise all medicine by discovering the world's first antibiotic, or bacteria killer. But I suppose that was exactly what I did." Fleming's accidental discovery and isolation of penicillin was the start of modern antibiotics and meant many diseases that were previously fatal became curable. For example, sanatoriums around the UK were closed down as the previously feared disease tuberculosis or consumption became curable.

Fleming died in 1955 and was buried in St Paul's Cathedral.

1. Why did he not start to train to become a doctor before the age of 22?
   a. He hadn't decided what he yet wanted to do.
   b. He couldn't afford to earlier.
   c. He became a bacteriologist first.
   d. He became a Captain in the First World War.

2. Why did he leave his role as lecturer at St Mary's hospital in 1914?
   a. To go to the frontline of the War.
   b. To join the Royal Air Force.
   c. To work with Sir Almroth Wright.
   d. As he was elected Professor of Bacteriology of the University of London.

3. In the third paragraph what is meant by the use of the word "halo"?
   a. A circle of bacteria.
   b. A circle clear of bacteria.
   c. The mould surrounding the bacteria.
   d. The bacteria surrounding the mould.

4. Why was the penicillin mould referred to as a contaminant?
   a. The mould was still contained in the dish.
   b. It's a type of fungus.
   c. The plate was growing bacteria not mould.
   d. It was releasing a substance that inhibited bacterial growth.

5. In the last paragraph, what is meant by the term "sanatorium"?
   a. A place where antibiotics, such as penicillin, were administered.
   b. A place where people were always kept inside.
   c. A place people were primarily treated for tuberculosis.
   d. A place with high energy consumption.

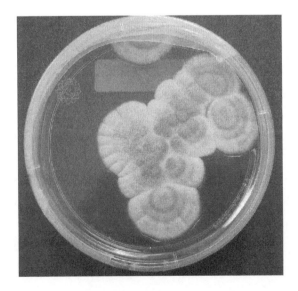

Choose the correct word in the passage below.

Knitting is the [6](art, craft, ability) of using needles to form a cloth. The wool is looped around a needle and [7](exchanged, switched, shuttled) from one needle to [8](another, the other, between each) as the cloth is formed. Knitting is [9](becoming, became, become) less common as it is now cheaper to buy a jumper than [10](made, done, make) it yourself.

Underline the odd one out.

11. aunt, daughter, niece, cousin, sister.

12. lark, robin, chaffinch, quail, dragonfly

13. pack, ream, pride, herd, colony

14. willowy, yew, larch, beech, birch

15. refer, tenet, repaper, tenant, reviver

Complete the words below to make a synonym of the word on the left.

16. **LIBEL**   s l _ _ _ e r

17. **FATHERLY**   p a _ _ _ n a l

18. **GOVERN**   m _ _ _ g e

19. **NAG**   _ _ d g e _

20. **CALLOUS**   c r _ _ _

Read the following newspaper article on a volcanic explosion, then answer the questions below.

Today one of Italy's worst fears are being realised as Mount Vesuvius erupts. It leaves the Italian government with the almost impossible task of evacuating over 3 million people living in the region.

Although the volcano has erupted numerous times since, none until now, has equalled the power and devastation caused by the great eruption of 79AD.

Earthquakes Signalled an Eruption

Earthquakes have been shaking the region for several weeks indicating that a large eruption was imminent. Yet the government failed to act and the result is now mass panic. David Walker, a volcanologist had been observing Vesuvius for over a year. The earthquakes, he warned the Italian authorities, were significant signs that the volcano could produce a violent explosion. The authorities however failed to heed Mr Walker's warning.

Naples in Darkness

Ash and debris have been spewing from the volcano for the last 3 days covering an area extending over 150km (93m) from the mountain. The number of people buried under the ash is as yet unknown however many homes have collapsed under the weight. The plume of debris rising from the summit is now estimated to stand at a height of 40km (24m). The effect has been to cast the area for a 100km (62m) radius into complete darkness.

Evacuation attempts are proving extremely difficult, not only because of the large number of people. Naples is located in a bay on the edge of the Tyrrhenian Sea preventing escape by road. Many ships and boats have been dispatched to the area but are now being showered with hot rocks and ashes putting crews at high risk.

Pyroclastic Flows the Greatest Threat

The greatest threat to the many remaining residents comes from pyroclastic flow. This phenomenon is what killed the majority of people in the 79AD eruption in the towns of Pompeii and Herculaneum. Hot ashes, rock and gas reaching temperatures of 1000°C (1,830°F) and moving at speeds of up to 750kph (450mph) kills everything in its path.

Mount Vesuvius is possibly the most famous volcano in the world. It was created by smaller eruptions and formed a cone rising from the centre of a caldera or crater. The crater was made when the mountain, then known as Mount Somma erupted over 17,000 years ago. Today fears are growing that when this eruption is over Vesuvius will not only kill many thousands but also leave a massive caldera of its own.

Plane Flights Disrupted

Additional problems have been caused as plane flights across Europe have been suspended due to low visibility and also fears of ash and debris stalling aircraft engines. It is predicted that the flight suspensions will have to be extended to the US and possibly around the world.

1. What is Mount Vesuvius?
    a. A mountain.
    b. A volcano.
    c. An earthquake.
    d. The cities of Pompeii and Herculaneum.

2. From the passage which of the following must be true?
    a. Vesuvius last erupted in 79AD.
    b. Vesuvius erupted without notice.
    c. Vesuvius was formed within the crater left by the explosion of Mount Somma.
    d. Volcanoes and earthquakes are completely different phenomena and are therefore unrelated.

3. Why is there a problem determining the number of people buried under the ash?
    a. The volcano is still erupting.
    b. People cannot travel by road as it is in a bay.
    c. There are too many people.
    d. There hasn't been time to start looking yet?

4. What does Pyroclastic "flow mean"?
    a. The movement of fire.
    b. A fast-moving current of hot gas and rock.
    c. Magma that goes very high into the air before coming back down to earth.
    d. Magma erupting from volcanos that have been made by the build-up of lava from previous eruptions (a composite volcano).

5. What could be used to replace the word "imminent" in the third paragraph?
    a. Possible.
    b. Violent.
    c. Needing action.
    d. About to happen.

Put in one or two missing letters, in the spaces below.

To [6]a__uire knowledge is the aim of many [7]univer__ity students. However, it is also important

that you can apply the [8]knowl__ge [9]l__rned. Therefore it is not just the [10]h__rding of

collectible facts.

Underline a word from each set of brackets to make a new, correctly spelled word.

11. (imp, clasp, reap)	(port, ped, ply)
12. (on, an, at)	(road, other, thing)
13. (sugar, sweet, honey)	(frosting, hair, comb)
14. (bread, butter, cheese)	(plate, cup, saucer)
15. (foot, tap, ramp)	(ped, sty, trace)

Underline the word below that is a synonym of the word on the left.

16. **RECOGNISABLE**   obvious, apparent, found, obscure

17. **CONTEST**   dispute, competitor, show, divulge

18. **CYNICAL**   trusting, supportive, hopeful, distrustful

19. **TANGIBLE**   abstract, hanging, concrete, earthen

20. **POIGNANT**   sentimental, moving, indifferent, numb

Read the poem "Father William" by Lewis Carroll.

"You are old, Father William," the young man said,
"And your hair has become very white;
And yet you incessantly stand on your head—
Do you think, at your age, it is right?"
"In my youth," Father William replied to his son,
"I feared it might injure the brain;
But now that I'm perfectly sure I have none,
Why, I do it again and again."

"You are old," said the youth, "as I mentioned before,
And have grown most uncommonly fat;
Yet you turned a back-somersault in at the door—
Pray, what is the reason of that?"
"In my youth," said the sage, as he shook his grey locks,
"I kept all my limbs very supple
By the use of this ointment—one shilling the box—
Allow me to sell you a couple."

"You are old," said the youth, "and your jaws are too weak
For anything tougher than suet;
Yet you finished the goose, with the bones and the beak:
Pray, how did you manage to do it?"
"In my youth," said his father, "I took to the law,
And argued each case with my wife;
And the muscular strength which it gave to my jaw
Has lasted the rest of my life."

"You are old," said the youth; "one would hardly suppose
That your eye was as steady as ever;
Yet you balanced an eel on the end of your nose—
What made you so awfully clever?"
"I have answered three questions, and that is enough,"
Said his father, "don't give yourself airs!
Do you think I can listen all day to such stuff?
Be off, or I'll kick you down-stairs!"

1. Which one is probably not a reason that the young man commented that Father William's hair is white?
   a. To stress that he is old.
   b. To make the poem more descriptive.
   c. It rhymes with right.
   d. To introduce the topic of the head.

2. Which of the following does *not* describe the father?
   a. Silly.
   b. Carefree.
   c. Puzzled.
   d. Active.

3. What does the word "supple" in the second stanza mean?
   a. Smooth.
   b. Flexible.
   c. Muscular.
   d. Tensile.

4. Father William eating a goose including the bones and the beak, is an example of?
   a. Alliteration.
   b. Hyperbole.
   c. Simile.
   d. Metaphor.

5. In the poem how does Father William see his age?
   a. An impediment to doing what he wants.
   b. A well-deserved rest from the constraints of youth.
   c. Finally attaining wisdom gained by living through his youth..
   d. An excuse to do whatever he likes.

Complete the words in the passage below.

Unicorns are [6]mythi☐☐☐ animals. They look like a horse but have a

[7]sing☐☐☐r horn on [8]th☐☐☐ [9]for☐☐☐☐d. A unicorn-like animal is

said to have existed called the *Elasmotherium*, however it appears to be more closely

related to the rhinocerous than the horse. [10]Fo☐☐☐l remains have been found from

Eastern Europe to China.

Jumbled Sentences

In each of the questions below, all the words except one can be made into a sentence.
Underline the word that is not used.

11. so much streets it that soon water rained the were flooded

12. two every swims for day he pool laps exercise

13. large eggs and has he brown three a chickens dog

14. to writes penfriend week she a too her once

15. holidays go to too seem quickly the is always

Antonyms

Choose the correct antonym for the word on the left

16. impartial   hostile, friendly, biased, worried

17. rotund   round, unimportant, sparse, thin

18. awe   shallow, contempt, difficult, trivial

19. abate   decrease, ebb, develop, revive

20. abridge   extend, stress, shorted, plunge

Read the following passage, then answer the questions below.

Why would one travel?

1   My knees rub the seat in front of me; the person besides me suffers from severe body
2   odour. The children behind me are having a loud argument with their mother about why
3   they need to go on an airplane, and why they aren't both allowed to sit by a window. The
4   mother responds, quietly and occasionally – insulated from the flow by her humming
5   headphones.
6   A lurch as the plane defeats gravity, the sickening lunge as we leave the earth. Our captain
7   crackles over the address system, a warm reassuring voice, a voice in another context that
8   could sell insurance. Assuring us that we are on the right plane, heading for the right
9   destination, and telling us about the awful weather we are experiencing. Then the plastic
10 smiles of the hosts and hostesses, passing out drinks, food and asking if we want to buy
11 anything from the catalogue.
12 I have had my bag examined, my person x-rayed and frisked, my destination checked and
13 ultimately my patience tested.
14 I look out of the cabin window I see green fields below, and small matchbox cars moving
15 along thin tiny roads. I see models of buildings out of the windows, getting smaller and
16 smaller.
17 The roll in front of me is stale, the warm moist cloth, given to me as well, I believe would
18 have more flavour. The coffee is watery, weak, the orange juice is warm, the air is
19 alternatively too cool, or too warm.
20 The landing is unremarkable, the screech of tyres hitting tarmac, the bump as the plane
21 comes to rest, tells me I am no longer weightless.
22 I leave the plane with my bag, moving sheep-like through the maze of the airport.
23 I pass into customs and immigration, standing in line: Step, shuffle, stand, step shuffle,
24 stand, smile for the passport officer. my passport is compared to myself, yes it is still me, I
25 saw myself in the mirror this morning, I'm certain that I haven't changed, apart from
26 growing grumpier.
27 Out into freedom, all of the paperwork done, all of the bureaucratic 'i's' dotted and 't's'
28 crossed. Down the complaining escalator, to the station, rushing for the waiting train. Then
29 waiting as it isn't ready to go yet.
30 The train ride is slightly more pleasant, the scenery outside is green. The cars and people
31 are back to their normal size. A cafe, near the station, seated, relaxing, watching the
32 people.
33 I sit, good coffee in hand, a diet destroying chocolate cake ready for eating: the cares of the
34 last hours leaving me.

1. How does the author feel about travelling?
    a. Hates travelling and would prefer not to.
    b. Loves travelling.
    c. Doesn't like the process but enjoys the results.
    d. Doesn't bother them.

2. In line 9, why does the author describe the cabin crew's smiles as plastic?
    a. The smile is forced, hiding their true feelings.
    b. They are wearing a lot of make-up.
    c. They have had plastic surgery.
    d. The author thinks they look like a child's doll from a playset.

3. What effect does the alliteration in lines 23 and 24 have?
    a. Makes it appear to go very quickly.
    b. Makes it appear to go very slowly.
    c. Stresses that he has not yet completed his journey.
    d. Creates the impression that the author is old.

4. In line 14, what type of word is "matchbox"?
    a. Noun.
    b. Verb.
    c. Adjective.
    d. Adverb.

5. What does the phrase, "i's dotted and t's crossed," in line 27 mean?
    a. Legal, such as to do with customs.
    b. To make sure all the small details are correct.
    c. Something that takes a long time.
    d. To fill in forms that have lots of questions on them.

Complete the words in the passage below.

Stop being such a ⁶nu☐☐☐☐ce!" said Mum. I wanted to be ⁷indepen☐☐☐t

and grown-up. However, I often found that when I ⁸l☐☐☐☐ned to my parents,

things worked out for the best. My parents tell me that I will grow up soon

⁹en☐☐☐h. The problem is, I'm not very ¹⁰pat☐☐☐t.

Complete the sentences below, so that the first part of the sentence and the second part of the

sentence are completed in the same way.

11. Hill is to (mountain, summit, valley) as pond is to (fish, sea, water).

12. Concave is to (blunt, down, inwards) as convex is to (outwards, sharp, glass).

13. Ring is to (telephone, finger, surround) as watch is to (look, participate, wrist).

14. Mobile is to (phone, toy, moving) as stationary is to (static, pens, crackling).

15. Tea is to (drink, dinner, leaf) as coffee is to (caffeine, powder, bean).

Choose the word which is the best synonym for the word on the left

16. **AVOID**   detour, seek, evade, clear

17. **TUG**   boat, rope, pull, safety

18. **REVOLVE**   turn, pistol, shoot, recoil

19. **PERIPHERY**   blunt, blade, sharp, edge

20. **IMPLICIT**   understand, lines, inferred, intertwine

Read the following excerpt from "The Happy Prince," by Oscar Wilde.

High above the city, on a tall column, stood the statue of the Happy Prince. He was gilded all over with thin leaves of fine gold, for eyes he had two bright sapphires, and a large red ruby glowed on his sword-hilt.

He was very much admired indeed. 'He is as beautiful as a weathercock,' remarked one of the Town Councillors who wished to gain a reputation for having artistic taste; 'only not quite so useful,' he added, fearing lest people should think him unpractical, which he really was not.

'Why can't you be like the Happy Prince?' asked a sensible mother of her little boy who was crying for the moon. 'The Happy Prince never dreams of crying for anything.'

'I am glad there is someone in the world who is quite happy', muttered a disappointed man as he gazed at the wonderful statue.

'He looks just like an angel,' said the Charity Children as they came out of the cathedral in their bright scarlet cloaks, and their clean white pinafores.

'How do you know?' said the Mathematical Master, 'you have never seen one.'

'Ah! but we have, in our dreams,' answered the children; and the Mathematical Master frowned and looked very severe, for he did not approve of children dreaming.

One night there flew over the city a little Swallow. His friends had gone away to Egypt six weeks before, but he had stayed behind, for he was in love with the most beautiful Reed. He had met her early in the spring as he was flying down the river after a big yellow moth, and had been so attracted by her slender waist that he had stopped to talk to her.

'Shall I love you said the Swallow', who liked to come to the point at once, and the Reed made him a low bow. So he flew round and round her, touching the water with his wings, and making silver ripples. This was his courtship, and it lasted all through the summer.

'It is a ridiculous attachment,' twittered the other Swallows, 'she has no money, and far too many relations;' and indeed the river was quite full of Reeds. Then, when the autumn came, they all flew away.

After they had gone he felt lonely, and began to tire of his lady-love. 'She has no conversation,' he said, 'and I am afraid that she is a coquette, for she is always flirting with the wind.' And certainly, whenever the wind blew, the Reed made the most graceful curtsies. I admit that she is domestic,' he continued, 'but I love travelling, and my wife, consequently, should love travelling also.'

'Will you come away with me?' he said finally to her; but the Reed shook her head, she was so attached to her home.

'You have been trifling with me,' he cried, 'I am off to the Pyramids. Good-bye!' and he flew away. All day long he flew, and at night-time he arrived at the city. 'Where shall I put up?' he said 'I hope the town has made preparations.'

Then he saw the statue on the tall column. 'I will put up there,' he cried; 'it is a fine position with plenty of fresh air.' So he alighted just between the feet of the Happy Prince.

'I have a golden bedroom,' he said softly to himself as he looked round, and he prepared to go to sleep; but just as he was putting his head under his wing, a large drop of water fell on him. 'What a curious thing!' he cried, 'there is not a single cloud in the sky, the stars are quite clear and bright, and yet it is raining. The climate in the north of Europe is really dreadful. The Reed used to like the rain, but that was merely her selfishness.'

Then another drop fell. 'What is the use of a statue if it cannot keep the rain off?' he said; 'I must look for a good chimney-pot,' and he determined to fly away. But before he had opened his wings, a third drop fell, and he looked up, and saw - Ah! What did he see?

The eyes of the Happy Prince were filled with tears, and tears were running down his golden cheeks. His face was so beautiful in the moonlight that the little Swallow was filled with pity.

'Who are you?' he said.
'I am the Happy Prince.'
'Why are you weeping then?' asked the Swallow; 'you have quite drenched me.'

'When I was alive and had a human heart,' answered the statue, 'I did not know what tears were, for I lived in the Palace of Sans-Souci where sorrow is not allowed to enter. In the daytime I played with my companions in the garden, and in the evening I led the dance in the Great Hall. Round the garden ran a very lofty wall, but I never cared to ask what lay beyond it, everything about me was so beautiful. My courtiers called me the Happy Prince, and happy indeed I was, if pleasure be happiness. So I lived, and so I died. And now that I am dead they have set me up here so high that I can see all the ugliness and all the misery of my city, and though my heart is made of lead yet I cannot choose but weep.'

'What, is he not solid gold?' said the Swallow to himself. He was too polite to make any personal remarks out loud.

'Far away,' continued the statue in a low musical voice,' far away in a little street there is a poor house. One of the windows is open, and through it I can see a woman seated at a table. Her face is thin and worn, and she has coarse, red hands, all pricked by the needle, for she is a seamstress. She is embroidering passion-flowers on a satin gown for the loveliest of the Queen's maids-of-honour to wear at the next Court-ball. In a bed in the corner of the room her little boy is lying ill. He has a fever, and is asking for oranges. His mother has nothing to give him but river water, so he is crying. Swallow, Swallow, little Swallow, will you not bring her the ruby out of my sword-hilt? My feet are fastened to this pedestal and I cannot move.'

1. Why was the Prince called "The Happy Prince?"
   a. He made people in the city feel happier.
   b. He looked happy on the top of the column.
   c. He was always happy when he lived in the palace.
   d. That was the name his parents gave him.

2. Why did the Mathematical master frown when the children said that the Happy Prince looked like an angel?
   a. He was upset that the children had been daydreaming.
   b. He only liked numbers.
   c. He felt that they should only think about facts and how to solve mathematical problems.
   d. He disagreed that the content of a dream could be used in a discussion.

3. Why did the sparrow choose to land on the statue?
   a. The location and appearance of the statue.
   b. He was lonely and wanted company.
   c. The look of the face in the moonlight.
   d. He wanted to meet such a famous statue.

4. Did the reed love the sparrow?
   a. No, but she enjoyed the attention.
   b. No, she can only move in the wind.
   c. Yes, but she is unable to leave the river.
   d. Yes, but she liked to be in the wind and the rain.

5. Why was the Prince no longer happy?
   a. The Charity Children thought he was an angel.
   b. People only saw his beauty and not his heart.
   c. He now knew that many people were sad.
   d. He was nothing more than a shelter for birds.

Choose the correct words in the passage below.

The young boy listened with [6](rapt, wrapped, rapped) attention to the

[7](teachers, teacher's, teachers') explanation. However, after a while his mind

[8](start, began, begin) to [9](wonder wander, surge) as he [10](thought, thinks, thinked) of

creative stories about aliens.

In these questions, find which letter can be moved from the first word to the second word to make two new words.
For example: bring   at
Answer: b (the new words are: ring, bat).

      11. route   cold   _____

      12. clone   cot   _____

      13. birds   coal   _____

      14. wheat   cost   _____

      15. cloud   sage   _____

Complete the antonyms of the words below:

      16. **RATIONAL**   a b _ _ _ d

      17. **DISTRACTED**   _ _ _ u s s e d

      18. **TRIVIAL**   c r _ _ _ a l

      19. **FLIMSY**   s t _ _ _ y

      20. **CREDIBLE**   d u b _ _ _ s

Verbal Ability – Test 32

Read the following excerpt adapted from "The Princess and the Goblin," by George MacDonald.

1   I have said the Princess Irene was about eight years old when my story begins. And this is
2   how it begins.

3   One very wet day, when the mountain was covered with mist which was constantly
4   gathering itself together into raindrops, and pouring down on the roofs of the great old
5   house, whence it fell in a fringe of water from the eaves all round about it, the princess
6   could not of course go out. She got very tired, so tired that even her toys could no longer
7   amuse her. You would wonder at that if I had time to describe to you one half of the toys
8   she had. But then, you wouldn't have the toys themselves, and that makes all the
9   difference: you can't get tired of a thing before you have it. It was a picture, though, worth
10 seeing—the princess sitting in the nursery with the sky ceiling over her head, at a great table
11 covered with her toys. If the artist would like to draw this, I should advise him not to meddle
12 with the toys. I am afraid of attempting to describe them, and I think he had better not try
13 to draw them. He had better not. He can do a thousand things I can't, but I don't think he
14 could draw those toys. No man could better make the princess herself than he could,
15 though—leaning with her back bowed into the back of the chair, her head hanging down,
16 and her hands in her lap, very miserable as she would say herself, not even knowing what
17 she would like, except it were to go out and get thoroughly wet, and catch a particularly nice
18 cold, and have to go to bed and take gruel. The next moment after you see her sitting there,
19 her nurse goes out of the room.

20 Even that is a change, and the princess wakes up a little, and looks about her. Then she
21 tumbles off her chair and runs out of the door, not the same door the nurse went out of, but
22 one which opened at the foot of a curious old stair of worm-eaten oak, which looked as if
23 never anyone had set foot upon it. She had once before been up six steps, and that was
24 sufficient reason, in such a day, for trying to find out what was at the top of it.

25 Up and up she ran—such a long way it seemed to her!—until she came to the top of the
26 third flight. There she found the landing was the end of a long passage. Into this she ran. It
27 was full of doors on each side. There were so many that she did not care to open any, but
28 ran on to the end, where she turned into another passage, also full of doors. When she had
29 turned twice more, and still saw doors and only doors about her, she began to get
30 frightened. It was so silent! And all those doors must hide rooms with nobody in them! That
31 was dreadful. Also the rain made a great trampling noise on the roof. She turned and
32 started at full speed, her little footsteps echoing through the sounds of the rain—back for
33 the stairs and her safe nursery.

34 She ran for some distance, turned several times, and then began to be afraid. Very soon she
35 was sure that she had lost the way back. Rooms everywhere, and no stair! Her little heart
36 beat as fast as her little feet ran, and a lump of tears was growing in her throat. But she was
37 too eager and perhaps too frightened to cry for some time. At last her hope failed her.

38 Nothing but passages and doors everywhere! She threw herself on the floor, and burst into
39 a wailing cry broken by sobs.

40 She did not cry long, however, for she was as brave as could be expected of a princess of her
41 age. After a good cry, she got up, and brushed the dust from her frock. Oh, what old dust it
42 was! Then she wiped her eyes with her hands, for princesses don't always have their
43 handkerchiefs in their pockets, any more than some other little girls I know of. Next, like a
44 true princess, she resolved on going wisely to work to find her way back: she would walk
45 through the passages, and look in every direction for the stair. This she did, but without
46 success. She went over the same ground again and again without knowing it, for the
47 passages and doors were all alike. At last, in a corner, through a half-open door, she did see
48 a stair. But alas! it went the wrong way: instead of going down, it went up. Frightened as
49 she was, however, she could not help wishing to see where yet further the stair could lead.
50 It was very narrow, and so steep that she went on like a four-legged creature on her hands
51 and feet.

52 When she came to the top, she found herself in a little square place, with three doors, two
53 opposite each other, and one opposite the top of the stair. She stood for a moment, without
54 an idea in her little head what to do next. But as she stood, she began to hear a curious
55 humming sound. Could it be the rain? No. It was much more gentle, and even monotonous
56 than the sound of the rain, which now she scarcely heard. The low sweet humming sound
57 went on, sometimes stopping for a little while and then beginning again. It was more like
58 the hum of a very happy bee that had found a rich well of honey in some globular flower,
59 than anything else I can think of at this moment. Where could it come from? She laid her ear
60 first to one of the doors to hearken if it was there—then to another. When she laid her ear
61 against the third door, there could be no doubt where it came from: it must be from
62 something in that room. What could it be? She was rather afraid, but her curiosity was
63 stronger than her fear, and she opened the door very gently and peeped in. What do you
64 think she saw? A very old lady who sat spinning.

65 Perhaps you will wonder how the princess could tell that the old lady was an old lady, when
66 I inform you that not only was she beautiful, but her skin was smooth. I will tell you more.
67 Her hair was combed back from her forehead and face, and hung loose far down and all
68 over her back. That is not much like an old lady—is it? Ah! but it was white almost as snow.
69 And although her face was so smooth, her eyes looked so wise that you could not have
70 helped seeing she must be old. The princess, though she could not have told you why, did
71 think her very old indeed—quite fifty, she said to herself. But she was rather older than that,
72 as you shall hear.

73 While the princess stared bewildered, with her head just inside the door, the old lady lifted
74 hers, and said, in a sweet, but old and rather shaky voice, which mingled very pleasantly
75 with the continued hum of her wheel: 'Come in, my dear; come in. I am glad to see you.'

76 That the princess was a real princess you might see now quite plainly; for she didn't hang on
77 to the handle of the door, and stare without moving, as I have known some do who ought to
78 have been princesses but were only rather vulgar little girls. She did as she was told,
79 stepped inside the door at once, and shut it gently behind her.

1. What was the main way that Irene knew that the lady was old?
    a. Her skin was smooth.
    b. Her hair was white.
    c. Her eyes looked wise.
    d. The way she spoke.

2. In line 9, when it says "you can't get tired of a thing before you have it," what does tired mean?
    a. Exhausted.
    b. Worn out.
    c. Unoriginal.
    d. Bored

3. Why did Irene's heart beat fast?
    a. Fear.
    b. Excitement.
    c. She was being brave.
    d. She was tired.

4. In line 65 what does the word "spinning" mean?
    a. She was turning around.
    b. She was making thread.
    c. She was playing with a child's toy.
    d. She was tossing a coin.

5. What voice is the passage in?
    a. 1st person.
    b. 2nd person.
    c. 3rd person.
    d. 4th person.

Complete the words in the passage below.

He was a very [6]confid _ _ _ young man. He was used to public speaking and his

[7]sp _ _ _hes were always very [8]elo _ _ _ n t and powerful. However, when speaking at

a [9]gover _ _ _ nt conference he found his knees a little shaky. This was despite the

[10]pract _ _ _ he had done the night before. He was pleased to find that he did not come

across as nervous as he felt.

Find a letter that ends the first word and starts the second word. Must be the same letter in each set of brackets.

11. l a m (   ) a l e   b u l (   ) i n

12. b a k e r (   ) e a r   s w a (   ) e l p

13. c a r (   ) o u t   s n i (   ) l e a

14. p l o (   ) i a l   s k i (   ) e f y

15. c h a s (   ) a l e   c h a r (   ) e l l o w

Underline the antonym of the words below.

16. **RESPONSE**   reply, statement, ask, stimulus

17. **CONDEMN**   reproach, acquit, err, correct

18. **VOWEL**   constant, consonant, constancy, consult

19. **VIRTUE**   merit, worth, vice, asset

20. **FLOW**   ebb, descend, brie, ohms

Read the poem "Foreign Lands by Robert Louis Stevenson, then answer the questions below.

1.   Up into the cherry tree

2.   Who should climb but little me?

3.   I held the trunk with both my hands

4.   And looked abroad in foreign lands.

5.   I saw the next door garden lie,

6.   Adorned with flowers, before my eye,

7.   And many pleasant places more

8.   That I had never seen before.

9.   I saw the dimpling river pass

10.   And be the sky's blue looking-glass;

11.   The dusty roads go up and down

12.   With people tramping in to town.

13.   If I could find a higher tree

14.   Farther and farther I should see,

15.   To where the grown-up river slips

16.   Into the sea among the ships,

17.   To where the road on either hand

18.   Lead onward into fairy land,

19.   Where all the children dine at five,

20.   And all the playthings come alive

1. In this poem what does the author mean by "foreign lands" in line 4?
    a. Places in other countries.
    b. Places that are unexplored.
    c. Somewhere the narrator has never been.
    d. Somewhere dangerous and difficult to get to.

2. What does the word "dimpling" tell up about the river?
    a. It's windy.
    b. It's smooth.
    c. It's not flat.
    d. It reflects faces of people who look into it.

3. Why is the river described as the sky's looking glass?
    a. It's blue.
    b. It looks the same as the sky.
    c. It contains animals that look at the sky.
    d. It reflects the image of the sky.

4. What could he see on the road?
    a. Flowers.
    b. Cars.
    c. Ships.
    d. Pedestrians.

5. If he could climb a higher tree, what would he like to see?
    a. The mouth of the river.
    b. Tall ships.
    c. The dimpling river.
    d. Children who eat at five.

Cloze

Complete the words in the passage below.

Very quickly, it became a matter of great amazement and the whole town became well [6]ac_

_ _ inted with the story, many [7]bu_ _ _ y engaged in conversation. Reports were

[8]trans_ _ _ ted between individuals long before it made the official news channels.

[9]Cons_ _ _ us that people would gossip and the story would become

[10]e_ _ _ erated an official version was quickly released.

Choose the word on the right that goes with both sets of brackets.

11. (monitor, check)   (ring, bracelet)   observe, detect, necklace, watch, bangle

12. (offensive, putrid)   (order, hierarchy)   number, list, rank, putrid, smelly

13. (back, end)   (raise, nurture)   hind, rear, last, tail, tend

14. (grind, polish)   (folder, notebook)   file, book, list, sharpen, directory

15. (extend, lengthen)   (pigeon, robin)   goose, augment, teal, egret, crane

Choose the synonym of the word on the left.

16. **SECRETE**   unrevealed, exude, furtive, cryptic

17. **DISPERSE**   scatter, gather, altitude, trite

18. **KINDLE**   fire, caring, ignite, quench

19. **RIVET**   welcome, incite, include, enthral

20. **MUNDANE**   ordinary, insipid, sharp, withered

Read the excerpt from "The Story of Doctor Dolittle" by Hugh Lofting and answer the questions below.

IT happened one day that the Doctor was sitting in his kitchen talking with the Cat's-meat-Man who had come to see him with a stomach-ache.

"Why don't you give up being a people's doctor, and be an animal-doctor?" asked the Cat's-meat-Man.

The parrot, Polynesia, was sitting in the window looking out at the rain and singing a sailor-song to herself. She stopped singing and started to listen.

"You see, Doctor," the Cat's-meat-Man went on, "you know all about animals—much more than what these here vets do. That book you wrote—about cats, why, it's wonderful! I can't read or write myself—or maybe I'd write some books. But my wife, Theodosia, she's a scholar, she is. And she read your book to me. Well, it's wonderful—that's all can be said—wonderful. You might have been a cat yourself. You know the way they think. And listen: you can make a lot of money doctoring animals. Do you know that? You see, I'd send all the old women who had sick cats or dogs to you. And if they didn't get sick fast enough, I could put something in the meat I sell 'em to make 'em sick, see?"

"Oh, no," said the Doctor quickly. "You mustn't do that. That wouldn't be right."

"Oh, I didn't mean real sick," answered the Cat's-meat-Man. "Just a little something to make them droopy-like was what I had reference to. But as you say, maybe it ain't quite fair on the animals. But they'll get sick anyway, because the old women always give 'em too much to eat. And look, all the farmers 'round about who had lame horses and weak lambs—they'd come. Be an animal-doctor."

When the Cat's-meat-Man had gone the parrot flew off the window on to the Doctor's table and said, "That man's got sense. That's what you ought to do. Be an animal-doctor. Give the silly people up—if they haven't brains enough to see you're the best doctor in the world. Take care of animals instead—They'll soon find it out. Be an animal-doctor."

"Oh, there are plenty of animal-doctors," said John Dolittle, putting the flower-pots outside on the window-sill to get the rain.

"Yes, there are plenty," said Polynesia. "But none of them are any good at all. Now listen, Doctor, and I'll tell you something. Did you know that animals can talk?"

"I knew that parrots can talk," said the Doctor.

"Oh, we parrots can talk in two languages—people's language and bird-language," said Polynesia proudly. "If I say, 'Polly wants a cracker,' you understand me. But hear this: Ka-ka oi-ee, fee-fee?"

"Good Gracious!" cried the Doctor. "What does that mean?"

"That means, 'Is the porridge hot yet?'—in bird-language."

"My! You don't say so!" said the Doctor. "You never talked that way to me before."

"What would have been the good?" said Polynesia, dusting some cracker-crumbs off her left wing. "You wouldn't have understood me if I had."

"Tell me some more," said the Doctor, all excited; and he rushed over to the dresser-drawer and came back with the butcher's book and a pencil. "Now don't go too fast—and I'll write it down. This is interesting—very interesting—something quite new. Give me the Birds' A.B.C. first— slowly now."

So that was the way the Doctor came to know that animals had a language of their own and could talk to one another. And all that afternoon, while it was raining, Polynesia sat on the kitchen table giving him bird words to put down in the book.

At tea-time, when the dog, Jip, came in, the parrot said to the Doctor, "See, he's talking to you."

"Looks to me as though he were scratching his ear," said the Doctor.

"But animals don't always speak with their mouths," said the parrot in a high voice, raising her eyebrows. "They talk with their ears, with their feet, with their tails—with everything. Sometimes they don't want to make a noise. Do you see now the way he's twitching up one side of his nose?"

"What's that mean?" asked the Doctor.

"That means, 'Can't you see that it has stopped raining?'" Polynesia answered. "He is asking you a question. Dogs nearly always use their noses for asking questions."

After a while, with the parrot's help, the Doctor got to learn the language of the animals so well that he could talk to them himself and understand everything they said. Then he gave up being a people's doctor altogether.

As soon as the Cat's-meat-Man had told everyone that John Dolittle was going to become an animal-doctor, old ladies began to bring him their pet pugs and poodles who had eaten too much cake; and farmers came many miles to show him sick cows and sheep.

One day a plow-horse was brought to him; and the poor thing was terribly glad to find a man who could talk in horse-language.

"You know, Doctor," said the horse, "that vet over the hill knows nothing at all. He has been treating me six weeks now—for spavins. What I need is spectacles. I am going blind in one eye. There's no reason why horses shouldn't wear glasses, the same as people. But that stupid man over the hill never even looked at my eyes. He kept on giving me big pills. I tried to tell him; but he couldn't understand a word of horse-language. What I need is spectacles."

"Of course—of course," said the Doctor. "I'll get you some at once."

1. Why does the Cat's-meat-Man suggest Dr Dolittle become an animal doctor?
    a. He is good with animals.
    b. He would make more money than with human patients.
    c. He has a good knowledge of animals.
    d. All of the above.

2. According to the passage how do animals communicate?
    a. Using sounds.
    b. With both sounds and movements.
    c. By moving about.
    d. They have two languages one they use to communicate with each other and one to communicate with humans.

3. Why did the farmers come many miles to bring Dr Dolittle their animals?
    a. Dr Dolittle could talk to the animals.
    b. He was more successful at treating them.
    c. They liked Dr Dolittle.
    d. The animals told their owners that they wanted to go there.

4. What was the problem with the horse?
    a. Swelling.
    b. Spavins.
    c. He was going blind.
    d. Both b and c.

5. What type of word is "spavins" in the final paragraph?
    a. Noun.
    b. Verb.
    c. Adjective.
    d. Adverb.

Write one or two letters into each space below.

Tom loved cooking. He was [6]fas___nated by how an [7]unapp___tising mixture can become

delicious after being put into the oven for a period of time. While a couple of friends initially

began to [8]ha___ass him when they found out about this hobby, they soon found it better to

[9]enc___rage him and enjoy the results! His most recent creation, a [10]brocco___i and leek

quiche, was a very enjoyable meal, especially when followed by home-made ice-cream.

Make a sentence out of all the words except one. Underline the word that is not used.

11.   forward looking over their were they to holidays

12.   on enjoys he games in weekends playing computer

13.   they packing house he busy were to move

14.   tried sing cough he started music but to to

15.   she flew last movie cinema she already watched had the when

Choose the antonym of the word on the left.

16.   **ABSOLVE**   polite, condemn, dissuade, earnest

17.   **SQUANDER**   cheap, expensive, guard, conserve

18.   **ELEVATE**   lower, bottom, short, lowly

19.   **ABOLISH**   quash, incite, sustain, dissolve

20.   **FOLLY**   build, wisdom, donkey, expert

Read the passage below about allotments and answer the questions below.

1   Allotment are plots of land made available to individuals for non-commercial gardening normally
2   of fruit and vegetables. Some allotments also allow bees and chickens to be kept. While
3   allotments in some form have been in existence since Anglo-Saxon times, the modern allotment
4   has its origins in the nineteenth century. Originally allotments were given to the labouring poor
5   so that they could grow food. In 1908 the Small Holdings and Allotments Act was promulgated
6   requiring local authorities to provide sufficient allotments for the demand by local residents. At
7   the end of the First World War allotments were made available to everyone including returning
8   service men. Statutory Allotments were established with the Allotments Act of 1925, which
9   could not be sold off by local authorities.
10
11 Allotments are leased from landlords, normally the local authority, so rent is paid. The rent
12 covers water and any other amenities provided.
13
14 The demand for allotments is rising and there are long waiting lists in many areas. In fact it is
15 thought that throughout the UK over 90 000 gardeners are currently on waiting lists, despite
16 there being approximately 330 000 plots.
17
18 People most commonly tend their allotments at weekends. The activities change throughout the
19 year. In winter many allotments lie dormant. Then when spring arrives the allotments become a
20 hive of activity with the land prepared and then the sowing of vegetables. Some vegetables
21 which were planted in the autumn are also harvested. In summer the crops need watering so
22 that they do not wilt and die. In late spring and autumn most of the crops are harvested and the
23 fresh fruit and vegetables are enjoyed. However, by planting a variety of crops, fresh fruit and
24 vegetables can be harvested over a large proportion of the year.

1. What is the main purpose of allotments?
    a. For people to grow food for their family.
    b. For people to grow food to make extra money.
    c. For the unemployed to have something productive to do.
    d. Both a and b.

2. What does the word promulgated in line 5 mean?
    a. Written.
    b. Thought of.
    c. Put a law into effect.
    d. Signed.

3. Who owns the allotment?
   a. The local authority.
   b. Private owners.
   c. The gardener who is producing the food.
   d. Either a or b.

4. What does the word dormant mean in line 19?
   a. Asleep.
   b. Alive but not actively growing.
   c. Temporarily inactive.
   d. Comatose.

5. What does the author think of allotments?
   a. The author doesn't like them.
   b. The author thinks they are useful if you need the food.
   c. The author thinks that they were useful in the past, particularly during the Great Depression after the First World War.
   d. The author has a positive view of allotments.

Complete the words in the passage below.

A newspaper is a daily or weekly publication containing news ⁶arti_ _ _ s,

⁷editor_ _ _ s, classified ads and other items. newspapers are generally divided into

sections such as: local and world news, television guide, education, entertainment and sport.

They also often contain a cartoon, comics and puzzles. Most newspapers also now have an

online ⁸pres_ _ _ _. The main revenue for the newspaper is not from the cover price but

from ⁹advert_ _ _ ments, including display ads, classified ads and their online ¹⁰equi_ _ _

ents.

In each question below, all the words but one are connected in some way. Underline the word
which is the odd one out.

16.   hammer, chisel, plane, ship, wrench

17.   cub, pony, calf, maggot, tadpole

18.   brook, stream, river, lake, creek

19.   slap, snug, strap, star, scold

20.   bicycle, car, motorbike, ferry, aeroplane

Choose the synonym of the word on the left.

21.   **ATTEST**   verify, scribe, proof, examine

22.   **AUGMENT**   argument, debate, enlarge, agreement

23.   **STELLAR**   terrestrial, metallic, star, extensive

24.   **QUEASY**   quash, suppress, adverse, nauseous

25.   **CURTAIL**   abridge, rudder, posterior, awning

Answers

Test 1

1. B
2. A
3. D
4. C
5. B
6. fortunate
7. throughout
8. dire
9. diseases
10. improve
11. their
12. ball
13. well
14. mean
15. watch
16. secure
17. arrogant
18. change
19. gain
20. clear

Test 2

1. B
2. A
3. B
4. C
5. C
6. C
7. beverage
8. beans
9. drunk
10. around
11. evidence
12. fifteenth
13. regularly
14. headache
15. break
16. hairy
17. hate
18. optional
19. dilute
20. miser

Test 3

1. B
2. A
3. B
4. D
5. C
6. glorious
7. shining
8. clear
9. friends
10. suddenly
11. eclipse
12. the
13. crew
14. learn
15. then
16. blossomed
17. create
18. baffle
19. thin
20. prior

Test 4

1. B
2. B
3. A
4. D
5. C
6. setting
7. singing
8. pool
9. bough
10. swooped
11. rain, bow
12. run, way
13. for, tune
14. rat, her
15. cot, ton
16. occupy
17. angry
18. poor
19. wild
20. view

Test 5

1. A
2. B
3. D
4. D
5. B
6. B
7. natural
8. persistence
9. lists
10. desire
11. successful
12. often
13. change
14. trip
15. desert
16. follow
17. shallow
18. vanish
19. natural
20. rare

Test 6

1. A
2. D
3. B
4. C
5. D
6. Solar
7. planet
8. energy
9. smaller
10. spherical
11. flat
12. kind
13. organ
14. soil
15. light
16. merge
17. poverty
18. gather
19. sunrise
20. mature

Test 7

1. C
2. D
3. D
4. B
5. A
6. September
7. divided
8. half
9. Autumn
10. Christmas
11. usually
12. for, go
13. pack, age
14. car, nation
15. me, an
16. Stiff
17. stable
18. despair
19. interior
20. conceal

Test 8

1. A
2. A
3. B
4. B
5. D
6. inhabitants
7. derelict
8. crumbling
9. hazardous
10. uncle
11. sole
12. palm
13. earn
14. post
15. thaw
16. insignificant
17. trivial
18. weep
19. ancient
20. peculiar

Test 9

1. C
2. A
3. C
4. D
5. B
6. attend
7. required
8. until
9. or
10. practical
11. trees, the
12. practicing, performance
13. and, is
14. slowed, on
15. young, games
16. framework
17. detailed
18. leaves
19. move
20. purchase

Test 10

1. C
2. A
3. C
4. B
5. B
6. quarter
7. caused
8. common
9. streets
10. rural
11. shore
12. mauve
13. rush
14. cast
15. thumb
16. precise
17. hilly
18. write
19. contract
20. depart

Test 11

1. B
2. D
3. A
4. C
5. D
6. sat
7. revised
8. neither
9. meant
10. friend's
11. stop
12. hospital
13. sunny
14. moon
15. stick
16. conclude
17. exact
18. final
19. reply
20. massive

Test 12

1. A
2. C
3. D
4. B
5. B
6. November
7. leased
8. immediately
9. barrels
10. explosion
11. stand
12. chair
13. record
14. root
15. level
16. throat
17. smash
18. stalk
19. clutch
20. applause

Test 13

1. C
2. A
3. D
4. C
5. B
6. frantically
7. decreasing
8. something
9. too
10. saw
11. identical
12. embarrass
13. neutral
14. digest
15. ladle
16. flexible
17. usual
18. robust
19. agree
20. mediocre

Test 14

1. C
2. D
3. D
4. B
5. A
6. shortage
7. malnourished
8. queue
9. rationing
10. improve
11. t
12. m
13. l
14. p
15. e
16. pit
17. seeming
18. unclear
19. consent
20. cunning

Test 15

1. A
2. D
3. D
4. D
5. C
6. practise
7. eat
8. already
9. meat
10. did
11. write
12. and
13. on
14. too
15. as
16. precious
17. close
18. pleasant
19. sorrow
20. brief

Test 16

1. B
2. C
3. B
4. A
5. D
6. flies
7. hour
8. drag
9. engrossed
10. become
11. fast
12. crane
13. date
14. rose
15. wound
16. valour
17. reveal
18. vague
19. assist
20. altitude

Test 17

1. C
2. A
3. D
4. D
5. B
6. complete
7. research
8. temperatures
9. sources
10. report
11. follow
12. weather
13. fray
14. alter
15. apple
16. nervous
17. anger
18. yearn
19. limit
20. determined

Test 18

1. B
2. D
3. D
4. A
5. B
6. oven
7. traditionally
8. salsa
9. selection
10. favourite
11. Monday
12. cow
13. so
14. ocean
15. fabric
16. displayed
17. hide
18. welcomed
19. deny
20. abstract

Test 19

1. B
2. D
3. A
4. C
5. B
6. appeared
7. became
8. from
9. variations
10. However
11. permit
12. bear
13. tick
14. punch
15. sound
16. retreat
17. flawed
18. soothing
19. steady
20. excited

Test 21

1. B
2. C
3. D
4. C
5. A
6. medium
7. text
8. frieze
9. portray
10. types
11. sell
12. move
13. student
14. enjoyed
15. accident
16. immense
17. cancel
18. compliant
19. starving
20. continue

Test 23

1. C
2. A
3. C
4. D
5. B
6. have
7. excellent
8. shone
9. flit
10. out
11. pound
12. roll
13. fast
14. maroon
15. mass
16. amiable
17. turmoil
18. imitation
19. borrow
20. passed

Test 20

1. B
2. C
3. A
4. B
5. D
6. central
7. tourist
8. theatres
9. speaking
10. million
11. very, left
12. for, by
13. down, came
14. your, always
15. did, ate
16. natural
17. enormous
18. contradict
19. flatter
20. ignorant

Test 22

1. D
2. C
3. A
4. A
5. B
6. pad
7. 11 o'clock
8. send
9. burnt
10. orbit
11. drink
12. made
13. theatre
14. act
15. was
16. quarrel
17. remain
18. ascend
19. usual
20. conceal

Test 24

1. B
2. A
3. B
4. D
5. C
6. transformed
7. advent
8. simultaneously
9. announced
10. congratulations
11. driver
12. athletics
13. tent
14. Earth
15. run
16. novice
17. lenient
18. dole
19. adamant
20. surpass

Test 25

1. B
2. D
3. B
4. A
5. C
6. loaded
7. capacity
8. profits
9. boarded
10. their
11. B
12. N
13. C
14. C
15. C
16. affluent
17. accidental
18. pristine
19. fine
20. certain

Test 27

1. B
2. A
3. B
4. C
5. C
6. art
7. shuttled
8. the other
9. becoming
10. make
11. cousin
12. dragonfly
13. ream
14. willowy
15. tenant
16. slander
17. paternal
18. manage
19. badger
20. cruel

Test 29

1. D
2. C
3. B
4. B
5. D
6. mythical
7. singular
8. their
9. forehead
10. fossil
11. water
12. pool
13. eggs
14. too
15. is
16. biased
17. thin
18. contempt
19. develop
20. extend

Test 26

1. A
2. C
3. D
4. B
5. B
6. transform
7. into
8. current
9. through
10. such as
11. does
12. lead
13. bark
14. mint
15. rest
16. tumblers
17. basin
18. shimmer
19. fast
20. angry

Test 28

1. B
2. C
3. A
4. B
5. D
6. acquire
7. university
8. knowledge
9. learned
10. hoarding
11. reapply
12. another
13. honeycomb
14. buttercup
15. tapped)
16. apparent
17. dispute
18. distrustful
19. concrete
20. moving

Test 30

1. C
2. A
3. B
4. C
5. B
6. nuisance
7. independent
8. listened
9. enough
10. patient
11. mountain, sea
12. inwards, outwards
13. finger, wrist
14. moving, static
15. leaf, bean
16. evade
17. pull
18. turn
19. edge
20. inferred

Test 31

1. C
2. A
3. A
4. B
5. C
6. rapt
7. teacher's
8. began
9. wander
10. thought
11. U
12. L
13. R
14. A
15. U
16. absurd
17. focussed
18. crucial
19. sturdy
20. dubious

Test 32

1. C
2. D
3. A
4. B
5. C
6. confident
7. speeches
8. eloquent
9. government
10. practice
11. B
12. Y
13. P
14. D
15. M
16. stimulus
17. acquit
18. consonant
19. vice
20. ebb

Test 33

1. C
2. C
3. D
4. D
5. A
6. acquainted
7. busily
8. transmitted
9. conscious
10. exaggerated
11. watch
12. rank
13. rear
14. file
15. crane
16. exude
17. scatter
18. ignite
19. enthral
20. ordinary

Test 34

1. D
2. B
3. B
4. C
5. A
6. ci (fascinated)
7. e (unappetising)
8. r (harass)
9. ou (encourage)
10. l (broccoli)
11. over
12. in
13. he
14. music
15. cinema
16. condemn
17. conserve
18. lower
19. sustain
20. wisdom

Test 35

1. A
2. C
3. D
4. C
5. D
6. articles
7. editorials
8. presence
9. advertisements
10. equivalents
11. ship
12. pony
13. lake
14. scold
15. bicycle
16. verify
17. enlarge
18. star
19. nauseous
20. abridge

Printed in Great Britain
by Amazon